THE ULTIMATE
NEW YORK JETS
TRIVIA BOOK

A Collection of Amazing Trivia Quizzes
and Fun Facts for Die-Hard Jets Fans!

Ray Walker

Exclusive Free Book

Crazy Sports Stories

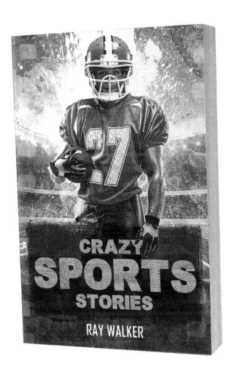

As a thank you for getting a copy of this book I would like to offer you a free copy of my book Crazy Sports Stories which comes packed with interesting stories from your favorite sports such as Football, Hockey, Baseball, Basketball and more.

Grab your free copy over at
RayWalkerMedia.com/Bonus

CONTENTS

INTRODUCTION

Kermit the Frog might have said it the best: It isn't easy being green. It certainly hasn't been easy to be a supporter of the New York Jets and proudly support Gang Green in recent years. As much as New York has had its pockets of success, much of the franchise's history has been about chasing the glory it achieved with Joe Namath. Such is the struggle of being a Jets fan in the 21st century.

This trivia book covers the entire history of the New York Jets, the good, the bad, and the ugly of this franchise's history over the next 12 chapters. Each chapter contains plenty of fun facts and interesting nuggets with the common goal of making you a more knowledgeable fan of the New York Jets. If we're successful, you will know far more about the Jets than when you first took this book off the shelf.

The questions in this book are designed to be a little bit difficult and keep you hanging on the edge of your seat as you engage with the facts. Each of the 12 chapters in this book focuses on a specific topic from the history of the franchise to specific positions and even the record book. In each chapter, there are 20 multiple-choice or true-false questions, the answers to those questions, followed by 10 interesting tidbits about that chapter's topic that will hopefully shed some light on the behind-the-scenes information. Please, do not be alarmed if some of these questions stump you; the whole point of the book is to help you learn more about your favorite team, so don't expect to ace every chapter.

We want you to learn something new by devouring this book, so that you can use your newfound knowledge to show off to your fellow fans in the New York metropolitan area and beyond. All of the information in this book is current as of the end of the 2020 season, so be warned that you might know more about the future by the time you pick up this book. All you need to do now is sit back, relax, and enjoy the hours of fun this book provides for the biggest New York Jets fans in the world.

CHAPTER 1:

ORIGINS & HISTORY

QUIZ TIME!

1. What was the original name of the franchise when the team was established in the AFL?

   a. New York Subways

   b. Brooklyn Dodgers

   c. New York Titans

   d. New York Yankees

2. When did the team's name change to New York Jets?

   a. 1965

   b. 1964

   c. 1963

   d. 1962

3. Who was the lead owner of the five-man group that bought the Jets from Harry Wismer?

   a. James Dolan

   b. Sonny Werblin

   c. Christopher Johnson

   d. Leon Hess

4. The Jets played their first four seasons at the Polo Grounds.

   a. True
   b. False

5. Who was the first coach of the New York Jets franchise?

   a. Weeb Ewbank
   b. Steve Sebo
   c. Bulldog Turner
   d. Sammy Baugh

6. Who did the Jets beat in their first game in 1960?

   a. Boston Patriots
   b. Houston Oilers
   c. Denver Broncos
   d. Buffalo Bills

7. Which was the first season after the AFL-NFL merger that the Jets qualified for the postseason?

   a. 1981
   b. 1982
   c. 1983
   d. 1984

8. The Jets won the first playoff game they ever played.

   a. True
   b. False

9. Which legendary college football coach was the Jets' head coach in 1976 for 13 games?

a. Joe Paterno

b. Bear Bryant

c. Lou Holtz

d. Bobby Bowden

10. Which of these coaches did NOT have at least a .500 record with the Jets?

   a. Bill Parcells

   b. Weeb Ewbank

   c. Sammy Baugh

   d. Al Groh

11. Adam Gase had the worst two-year winning percentage of any coach in Jets history.

   a. True

   b. False

12. In which season did the Jets move from Shea Stadium to Giants Stadium?

   a. 1985

   b. 1983

   c. 1986

   d. 1984

13. Who did the Jets play in their final game at Giants Stadium before moving to MetLife Stadium?

   a. New England Patriots

   b. Miami Dolphins

   c. Cincinnati Bengals

   d. Buffalo Bills

14. Which team has the Jets defeated the most in their history?

    a. New England Patriots
    b. Miami Dolphins
    c. Indianapolis Colts
    d. Buffalo Bills

15. Who scored the first touchdown in Jets history?

    a. Don Maynard
    b. Art Powell
    c. Al Dorow
    d. Pete Hart

16. Who was the Jets' head coach the last time the team won the AFC East?

    a. Herm Edwards
    b. Rex Ryan
    c. Eric Mangini
    d. Bill Parcells

17. The Jets have a winning record against the Giants since the two teams began sharing a stadium.

    a. True
    b. False

18. Who is NOT one of the three players to play for the Jets during all 10 seasons in the AFL?

    a. Larry Grantham
    b. Don Maynard
    c. Bill Mathis
    d. Paul Rochester

19. How many times have the Jets won at least 10 games during a season?

    a. 9
    b. 11
    c. 13
    d. 15

20. Current Jets owner Woody Johnson returned to the team in 2021 after spending three years as the United States ambassador to which European nation?

    a. United Kingdom
    b. Belgium
    c. Ireland
    d. Luxembourg

QUIZ ANSWERS

1. C – New York Titans

2. C – 1963

3. B – Sonny Werblin

4. A – True

5. D – Sammy Baugh

6. D – Buffalo Bills

7. A – 1981

8. A – True

9. C – Lou Holtz

10. B – Weeb Ewbank

11. B – False

12. D – 1984

13. C – Cincinnati Bengals

14. D – Buffalo Bills

15. C – Al Dorow

16. A – Herm Edwards

17. B – False

18. D – Paul Rochester

19. B – 11

20. A – United Kingdom

DID YOU KNOW?

1. When the American Football League was creating its eight charter franchises, New York made a strong push to be included. Harry Wismer secured the charter for the franchise in 1959 and named the team the New York Titans after the latest addition to the US strategic missile arsenal, the Titan, but he also claimed that "Titans are bigger and stronger than Giants," as a jab at the other football team in town, the New York Giants.

2. Wismer was an extremely controversial owner, especially when it came to paying his players and coaches. His paychecks notoriously bounced several times during his tenure as owner, and he was removed as owner in 1962 after being unable to pay the players for the final four games of the season. The AFL assumed control of the finances to ensure the players were paid, and, by the middle of 1963, new owners—a group headed by Sonny Werblin—had assumed control of the team for $1 million.

3. Werblin and his ownership group made a lot of changes to the franchise upon taking over operations in 1963. His first act was to change the name of the team to the New York Jets, and, on the same day, he hired Weeb Ewbank as the team's coach. A year later, he moved the team from the Polo Grounds to Shea Stadium, the brand new Queens stadium built for the New York Mets. After averaging

roughly 5,000 fans per game at the Polo Grounds, the Jets had more than 45,000 spectators show up for their first game against the Denver Broncos.

4. Only 13 players who played under the Titans moniker were still on the team in 1963 when the franchise opened the season as the Jets. Four players who appeared for the Titans—linebacker Larry Grantham, running back Bill Mathis, receiver Don Maynard, and defensive lineman Paul Rochester—are among the 20 players who played all 10 seasons of the AFL's existence before the league merged with the NFL.

5. The Titans got off to an excellent start in their inaugural season, with a dominating 27-3 win over Buffalo. After the Bills scored the first points of the game, New York took control with two Bill Shockley field goals, a pair of Al Dorow touchdown runs, and a 13-yard pass from Dick Jamieson to Art Powell. The Titans actually won four of their first six games before slumping and finishing at an even 7-7 in their first season.

6. Nearly five decades since he roamed the sidelines as the Jets coach, no one has come close to touching Weeb Ewbank's record for most wins by a head coach in franchise history. Ewbank actually had a losing record of 71-77-6 in 11 seasons with New York and put together just three winning seasons, but he has 18 more wins than any other coach the Jets have had in their history. He is also still the only coach to lead the Jets to the Super Bowl, leading

New York to an 11-3 record before beating the favored Colts in Super Bowl III.

7. Sonny Werblin had a falling out with his partners because they were upset about him making decisions about the franchise without consulting them. Finally, he was bought out in 1968, and Leon Hess became the principal owner until he bought out everyone else and became the sole owner of the franchise from 1984 until he died in 1999. Woody Johnson then bought the team for $635 million, outbidding Charles Dolan, who owned the Knicks and Rangers, for the NFL franchise. In all, more than 20 potential bidders inquired about the price after Hess's passing.

8. The downside to the Jets moving to Shea Stadium was their place as secondary tenants of the facility. They could not play any home games until the Mets had finished their season, putting a lot of stress on their schedule early in the season with road games. It all boiled over in 1983 when the mayor of New York, Ed Koch, failed to come to an agreement with Jets owner Leon Hess for a new stadium for the Jets. Koch announced, without Hess's knowledge, that the Jets were planning to move to Giants Stadium in New Jersey, and, within two weeks, the agreement was in place for the Jets and Giants to share a stadium, a relationship that is still in place today at MetLife Stadium.

9. It's been more than 30 years since the New York Jets last had a tie game, which came October 2, 1988, at home

against Kansas City. The Jets held a 17-3 lead early in the fourth quarter, but the Chiefs scored twice to tie the game and neither team was able to score in the 15-minute overtime period.

10. The Jets have been one of the more unsuccessful franchises of the Super Bowl era despite having won a Lombardi Trophy. New York has just nine seasons with at least 10 wins since the AFL-NFL merger in 1970 and has made the playoffs just 14 times in 55 years of the Super Bowl era. The Jets have also won their division just twice since the merger (1998 and 2002) while also losing in the conference championship game four times in that span (1982, 1998, 2009, and 2010).

CHAPTER 2:

NUMBERS GAME

QUIZ TIME!

1. What punter was the only other player besides Don Maynard to wear number 13 for the Jets?

    a. Chuck Ramsey

    b. Duane Carrell

    c. Dave Jennings

    d. Greg Gantt

2. Which early Jets quarterback wore number 12 before Joe Namath made the number famous for the franchise?

    a. Lee Grosscup

    b. Al Dorow

    c. Mike Taliaferro

    d. Dick Wood

3. Mike Nugent was the Jets player who most recently wore number 1.

    a. True

    b. False

4. Which defensive back wore number 28 before Curtis Martin retired it in the late 1990s?

   a. Darrol Ray
   b. Burgess Owens
   c. Lee Riley
   d. Bill Baird

5. Which Jets starting quarterback was the first to wear number 14 for the Jets?

   a. Johnny Green
   b. Dickie Jamieson
   c. Al Woodall
   d. Richard Todd

6. Though he wasn't technically the first to wear the number for the Jets, what number did Vinny Testaverde become the first Jets player to wear for multiple games?

   a. 15
   b. 16
   c. 17
   d. 18

7. Kliff Kingsbury's only NFL appearance came with the Jets in 2005, and he wore number 3 in that game.

   a. True
   b. False

8. Which number did both Ty Law and Ed Reed wear during their stints with the Jets?

a. 20

b. 21

c. 22

d. 24

9. Who did NOT wear the number 24 for the Jets before Darrelle Revis arrived in New York?

  a. Freeman McNeil

  b. Johnny Sample

  c. Ray Mickens

  d. Bill Mathis

10. What number did both Dainard Paulson and James Hasty wear with the Jets?

  a. 33

  b. 37

  c. 40

  d. 42

11. Which of these Jets did NOT wear number 57 during their career in New York?

  a. Mo Lewis

  b. Bart Scott

  c. John Little

  d. Dan Alexander

12. Which number did Winston Hill wear while protecting Joe Namath's blindside for all those seasons with the Jets?

  a. 70

  b. 73

c. 75

d. 77

13. No one has worn number 80 since Wayne Chrebet's retirement.

   a. True

   b. False

14. What number did Super Bowl hero George Sauer wear for the Jets?

   a. 81

   b. 82

   c. 83

   d. 84

15. What number did the Jets retire in honor of Dennis Byrd?

   a. 88

   b. 90

   c. 92

   d. 93

16. What number did Mark Gastineau wear while terrorizing opposing quarterbacks for the Jets?

   a. 99

   b. 97

   c. 96

   d. 94

17. What were the two main colors of the New York Titans?

   a. Green and white

   b. Red and black

c. Blue and red

d. Blue and gold

18. In which year did the Jets introduce their Kelly green helmet?

    a. 1967

    b. 1972

    c. 1974

    d. 1978

19. Bill Parcells immediately got rid of the Jets logo with the airplane and reverted to the Super Bowl era look in his first season as coach.

    a. True

    b. False

20. When the Jets unveiled their new uniforms in 2019, what was the name given to the new black uniforms?

    a. Stealth black

    b. Gotham black

    c. Midnight black

    d. Blackout

QUIZ ANSWERS

1. C – Dave Jennings

2. B – Al Dorow

3. B – False

4. A – Darrol Ray

5. D – Richard Todd

6. B – 16

7. A – True

8. C – 22

9. D – Bill Mathis

10. C – 40

11. D – Dan Alexander

12. C – 75

13. A – True

14. C – 83

15. B – 90

16. A – 99

17. D – Blue and gold

18. D – 1978

19. B – False

20. A – Stealth black

DID YOU KNOW?

1. The number 13 is very unlucky for many people, but, for that exact reason, Don Maynard was very superstitiously positive about the number. Not only did he don the number on the field, but it also became important in his record-breaking pursuit of the career receptions record. He broke the NFL record in the 13th game of his 13th season with the Jets.

2. In the years following Joe Namath's retirement, the burning question was when the Jets would retire his number 12. The franchise's stance was consistently that it would wait for Namath to be elected into the Hall of Fame. Four months after Namath received the call that he had been elected, the Jets announced they would retire the number 12 in Namath's honor. He was the first New York Jets player to receive the honor.

3. Dennis Byrd is the latest of the five Jets who have had their jersey numbers retired. His number 90 was retired in 2012, though no one had worn it in the 20 years between the retirement ceremony and his career-ending injury. Byrd sent Rex Ryan the jersey that was torn off his body in 1992 when he was injured while chasing the quarterback in a game against the Kansas City Chiefs.

4. Joe Klecko was the first defensive player to have his number retired by the Jets and third player overall. His

number 73 was worn by two different players after he left the Jets, offensive tackle David Williams for two seasons, from 1996 to 1997, and offensive lineman Siupeli Malamala in 1999.

5. Curtis Martin had a tough time deciding what jersey number to wear in New England after being drafted. He couldn't wear the number 29 that he wore in college, so he had to decide between 26 and 28. He asked his pastor about the decision, and the pastor told him to choose number 28 because of the 28th chapter of Deuteronomy. That chapter discusses the importance of obeying God, and it became a pregame habit for Martin to read the chapter before games.

6. After the Jets drafted Keyshawn Johnson in 1996, the rookie receiver shrewdly waited to pick his new number. He wanted to wear number 3 as he had in college, but the NFL denied his request and said he could choose a number between 10 and 19 if all the numbers in the 80s were taken by the team that drafted him. So Johnson held out selecting his jersey number until after all of the 80s were handed out by the Jets at training camp and settled on number 19, which he was allowed to then keep after some numbers in the 80s became available.

7. It is not uncommon for players to buy a jersey number from a new teammate if that number means something to them. For example, after wearing number 87 for four years in Denver, Eric Decker gave tight end Jeff Cumberland

$25,000 and paid for a steak dinner in exchange for number 87 when Decker joined the Jets.

8. Jamal Adams has always worn the number 33 to honor his father, George Adams. The elder Adams was a 1st round pick of the Giants but chipped his pelvis during training camp his rookie year, which derailed his career. Adams wore the number proudly for the green-and-white until his contentious divorce from the team in 2020.

9. In July 2020, CBS Sports ranked the best NFL players ever to wear every jersey number from 1 to 99, and four Jets made the list. Of those listed, only Larry Grantham (60) spent a majority of his career with the Jets, and the other three didn't spend much time in New York. Brett Favre (4) played for the Jets in 2008 after being acquired from the Packers, Steve Atwater (27) played 11 games for New York in 1999, and Ronnie Lott (42) finished his career with two productive seasons for the Jets.

10. The New York Titans wore navy blue and gold uniforms, but the colors changed to Kelly green and white under new owner Sonny Werblin in 1963. The owner chose those colors because of his affinity for St. Patrick's Day, which was also his birthday. The original logo in 1963 was a green airplane with the words Jets in it before it was changed in 1964 to the recognizable "NY Jets" inside a green football.

CHAPTER 3:

CALLING THE SIGNALS

QUIZ TIME!

1. No Jets quarterback has ever thrown for 4,000 yards in a season.

    a. True
    b. False

2. Who holds the Jets' record for most passing yards in a game?

    a. Mark Sanchez
    b. Ryan Fitzpatrick
    c. Joe Namath
    d. Ken O'Brien

3. Who was the last Jets quarterback to be named to the Pro Bowl?

    a. Ryan Fitzpatrick
    b. Ken O'Brien
    c. Boomer Esiason
    d. Brett Favre

4. What is the Jets' record for most passing touchdowns in a game, held by both Joe Namath and Brett Favre?

   a. 6
   b. 5
   c. 7
   d. 4

5. Who currently holds the Jets' record for most passing touchdowns in a season when he became the only Jets quarterback to throw for at least 30 touchdowns in a season?

   a. Ryan Fitzpatrick
   b. Sam Darnold
   c. Brett Favre
   d. Richard Todd

6. Which quarterback was sacked the most times in Jets history?

   a. Chad Pennington
   b. Joe Namath
   c. Ken O'Brien
   d. Richard Todd

7. Who was the starting quarterback in the Titans' first game in 1960?

   a. Joe Namath
   b. Dick Jamieson
   c. Al Dorow
   d. Dick Wood

8. Brett Favre is the most accurate Jets quarterback in history who has thrown at least 500 passes for the franchise.

   a. True
   b. False

9. Which quarterback has the most wins in Jets history while also holding an overall winning record as the Jets' starter?

   a. Mark Sanchez
   b. Joe Namath
   c. Chad Pennington
   d. Vinny Testaverde

10. Who is the Jets' all-time leader in rushing yards for a quarterback?

    a. Al Dorow
    b. Joe Namath
    c. Richard Todd
    d. Mark Sanchez

11. Al Dorow led the league in passing touchdowns in 1960 when he threw how many touchdowns during the inaugural New York Titans season?

    a. 20
    b. 22
    c. 24
    d. 26

12. How many touchdown passes did Joe Namath throw in his career to set the Jets' record?

a. 140

b. 150

c. 160

d. 170

13. In which year did Joe Namath NOT lead the league in passing yards?

a. 1972

b. 1968

c. 1967

d. 1966

14. Who is the only quarterback aside from Joe Namath to be named to multiple Pro Bowls with the Jets?

a. Vinny Testaverde

b. Chad Pennington

c. Ken O'Brien

d. Richard Todd

15. The only season in which Ken O'Brien threw more interceptions than touchdowns was his rookie year in 1984.

a. True

b. False

16. Which quarterback started the season opener for the Jets in 1998, before Vinny Testaverde took over in the third game of the season and led the Jets to a division title?

a. Glenn Foley

b. Ray Lucas

c. Neil O'Donnell

d. Rick Mirer

17. Chad Pennington won the NFL Comeback Player of the Year twice during his career. Which season did he win it when he was with the Jets?

    a. 2005

    b. 2006

    c. 2007

    d. 2008

18. Against which team did Mark Sanchez commit the infamous "butt fumble" on Thanksgiving night in 2012?

    a. Buffalo Bills

    b. Miami Dolphins

    c. New England Patriots

    d. Pittsburgh Steelers

19. The Jets traded for Ryan Fitzpatrick.

    a. True

    b. False

20. How many times did Sam Darnold throw for 300 yards in a game while with the Jets?

    a. 0

    b. 2

    c. 3

    d. 4

QUIZ ANSWERS

1. B – False

2. C – Joe Namath

3. D – Brett Favre

4. A – 6

5. A – Ryan Fitzpatrick

6. C – Ken O'Brien

7. B – Dick Jamieson

8. A – True

9. D – Vinny Testaverde

10. C – Richard Todd

11. D – 26

12. D – 170

13. B – 1968

14. C – Ken O'Brien

15. B – False

16. A – Glenn Foley

17. B – 2006

18. C – New England Patriots

19. A – True

20. D – 4

DID YOU KNOW?

1. Al Dorow was the franchise's first starting quarterback, but it took some freak luck for Dorow to even play quarterback in the first place. He was a running back in high school and at Michigan State for his first year and a half. But, when the Spartans had three quarterbacks injured in a game, they turned to Dorow. He learned the position in a week and led Michigan State to a win over Penn State and then kept learning and improving until he made his mark in Canada and the AFL as a quarterback.

2. Joe Namath's accomplishments on the field are perhaps more impressive considering his exploits off of it. He was famous for his nocturnal habits and staying out late at clubs and bars, normally with at least one lady. In a 2019 autobiography, he admitted, "I was in my early 20s when this fame hit, living in one of the sexiest cities in the world, so it felt natural to turn toward it and not shy away." Drinking had caused Namath some issues at Alabama when he was suspended for the final two games of the 1963 season for drinking. He then battled alcoholism after his playing career was over, but in between, he was everything the Jets could have asked for in a quarterback as the first player ever to throw for 4,000 yards in a professional football season.

3. Richard Todd was the first in a string of quarterbacks hoping to replace Joe Namath in Kelly green as the Jets'

starter. Though he had his share of great moments, he also had his share of ugly ones. That included a fight with a reporter from the *New York Post* that ended when Todd shoved him into a locker, and the reporter had to be treated at a local hospital. Todd had refused to speak with the reporter, claiming his articles were unfair to Todd, and, after asking the reporter to leave several times, he resorted to violence. The case was later dropped, but it was a sign of the quarterback struggles that would befall the franchise.

4. Ken O'Brien's second season in the league was sabotaged by a trial for a misdemeanor that forced him to miss all of training camp in 1984. He was expected to be the Jets' starter that season, but, with O'Brien in court all day every day for four weeks, Pat Ryan took over for New York in 1984. O'Brien was able to show off his potential after Ryan was injured later that season, then he exploded onto the scene with a massive year in 1985. He led the Jets to an 11-5 record that season and was named to his first Pro Bowl after throwing for 3,888 yards, 25 touchdowns, and just eight interceptions in 16 starts.

5. Vinny Testaverde was sitting comfortably on his coach for much of 2005 after no one pursued him as a 41-year-old free agent quarterback. When Chad Pennington and Jay Fiedler both went down with shoulder injuries, Testaverde called the Jets and told them he was available. His advances were rebuffed at first because the Jets turned to someone who had been in an NFL training camp, but they eventually changed course. In his first

start for the Jets that season, he led New York to a 14-12 win over Tampa Bay. It was Testaverde's only win that year for the Jets as he went 1-3 in four starts with just one touchdown pass and six interceptions.

6. Chad Pennington has an interesting story about his rookie hazing with the Jets in 2000. The quarterback was desperate to not shave his head, so he was willing to do almost anything to keep his hair. His veteran teammates made him wear his helmet everywhere for 24 hours from the shower to sleeping at night. Pennington was even pulled over during that period, and he was ticketed when he refused to remove his helmet for the officer for fear of what would happen if he was caught without his helmet on.

7. Brett Favre's tenure with the Jets is not remembered fondly because of how poorly Favre played over the final month of the 2008 season. But Favre led New York to an 8-3 record in his first 11 games and electrified the fan base with plays Jets fans only dreamed of seeing from their team. He was magical, and the Jets were on the cusp of an extraordinary season before Favre tore a tendon in his biceps. That version of Favre failed the Jets because he lost control of where he was throwing the ball at times, and the quarterback admitted in 2016 that he probably should have sat out after the injury and ended his ironman streak because he was doing more harm than good. Instead, he left a sour taste in the mouths of Jets fans as New York missed the playoffs yet again.

8. Mark Sanchez did a lot of good things as the Jets' starting quarterback, notably guiding the franchise to consecutive AFC Championship Games. But Sanchez will forever be memorialized by the "butt fumble" when his attempt to turn a broken play into a positive against New England on Thanksgiving Day 2012 went horribly wrong. Sanchez was supposed to hand off the ball to fullback Lex Hilliard, but the two miscommunicated and went opposite ways. So Sanchez just turned around and tried to at least pick up a few yards on a quarterback scramble. Instead, the quarterback plowed into the back of Brandon Moore, and the ball popped free. The Patriots scooped up the fumble and returned it for a touchdown to take a 21-0 lead.

9. Geno Smith's tenure with the Jets is best remembered for a teammate breaking the quarterback's jaw during a locker-room fight. During training camp in 2015, Smith and defensive lineman IK Enemkpali got into an argument that ended when Enemkpali punched Smith in the face and broke his jaw. The two were arguing over $600, which Enemkpali believed Smith owed him for a plane ticket to Enemkpali's camp that offseason that Smith had to withdraw from participating in due to a death in the family. The punch dramatically altered Smith's career in New York as Ryan Fitzpatrick came in and won the starting job during a sensational season with the Jets, and Smith never regained the job.

10. Sam Darnold has been a victim of the poor situation around him, but he's had his bright spots. However, one of

those moments was not in 2019 when Darnold told coaches he was "seeing ghosts" on the field during a 33-0 loss to the Patriots in which Darnold threw four interceptions. The comments were picked up by the microphone Darnold was wearing for NFL Films and were broadcasted on ESPN during their telecast of the *Monday Night Football* game between the Jets and New England. The comment became a meme and came to define Darnold's struggles with the Jets, though many claimed ESPN made a serious error in judgment by airing the comments during the broadcast.

CHAPTER 4:

BETWEEN THE TACKLES

QUIZ TIME!

1. Who holds the Jets' record for most rushing yards in a single game?

   a. Curtis Martin
   b. Thomas Jones
   c. Isaiah Crowell
   d. Shonn Greene

2. What is the Jets' record for most rushing touchdowns in a season?

   a. 11
   b. 12
   c. 13
   d. 14

3. Who was the first Jets player to rush for 1,000 yards in a single season?

   a. Emerson Boozer
   b. John Riggins

c. Freeman McNeil
  d. Bill Mathis

4. How long was Johnny Johnson's rush against the Bears in 1994 to set the Jets' record for longest run from scrimmage?

  a. 97 yards
  b. 94 yards
  c. 90 yards
  d. 87 yards

5. Johnny Johnson's franchise-record rush is the only one to eclipse 80 yards.

  a. True
  b. False

6. Who was the first Jets running back to rush for 1,000 yards in consecutive seasons?

  a. Freeman McNeil
  b. Curtis Martin
  c. Bill Mathis
  d. Adrian Murrell

7. Which running back was first to be named a First Team All-Pro with the Jets?

  a. Freeman McNeil
  b. Curtis Martin
  c. Bill Mathis
  d. Matt Snell

8. How many Jets running backs have rushed for at least 1,000 yards and at least 10 touchdowns in the same season?

    a. 2
    b. 3
    c. 4
    d. 5

9. No Jets running back has ever averaged more than 100 yards per game in a season.

    a. True
    b. False

10. Who was the last running back the Jets selected in the first two rounds of the NFL Draft?

    a. Shonn Greene
    b. Bilal Powell
    c. LaMont Jordan
    d. Blair Thomas

11. Matt Snell set his career high for rushing yards in a season as a rookie in 1964 when he ran for how many yards?

    a. 929
    b. 948
    c. 962
    d. 981

12. What is John Riggins's actual first name?

    a. Robert
    b. John

c. James

d. Roger

13. What was impressive about the 1979 season for Clark Gaines?

    a. Fewest carries to lead Jets in rushing
    b. Fewest games played to lead Jets in rushing
    c. Fewest yards ever to lead Jets in rushing
    d. Led Jets in rushing without scoring a touchdown

14. In which year did Freeman McNeil lead the NFL in rushing yards?

    a. 1985
    b. 1984
    c. 1983
    d. 1982

15. Curtis Martin holds the top four spots in the Jets' record book for rushing yards in a season.

    a. True
    b. False

16. In which season was Curtis Martin named a First Team All-Pro running back?

    a. 1998
    b. 2001
    c. 2003
    d. 2004

17. How did the Jets acquire Thomas Jones?

a. Free agent

b. Trade

c. Undrafted free agent

d. Draft

18. In which two years did Shonn Greene go over 1,000 yards on the ground for the Jets?

a. 2009 and 2010

b. 2010 and 2011

c. 2011 and 2012

d. 2012 and 2013

19. Chris Ivory was the Jets running back who most recently rushed for 1,000 yards in a season.

a. True

b. False

20. Which Jets running back holds the record for most kick return touchdowns in franchise history?

a. Joe McKnight

b. Bruce Harper

c. Jo-Jo Townsell

d. Leon Washington

QUIZ ANSWERS

1. C – Isaiah Crowell

2. D – 14

3. B – John Riggins

4. C – 90 yards

5. A – True

6. A – Freeman McNeil

7. C – Bill Mathis

8. A – 2

9. B – False

10. C – LaMont Jordan

11. B – 948

12. A – Robert

13. D – Led Jets in rushing without scoring a touchdown

14. D – 1982

15. B – False

16. D – 2004

17. B – Trade

18. C – 2011 and 2012

19. A – True

20. D – Leon Washington

DID YOU KNOW?

1. Bill Mathis was one of seven players who played in all 10 years of the AFL for the same franchise. He missed just three games during his 10 seasons with the Jets, all of which came in 1962 due to a knee injury. Mathis was assigned to room with Joe Namath on road trips to keep an eye on Namath and prevent as much trouble as possible with the star quarterback.

2. Emerson Boozer was a close personal friend of Clarence Clemons from their time at Maryland State. Clemons was among the linemen tasked with paving the way for Boozer in the backfield, and the two remained friends once Clemons's football career was over. One night when the two friends met up after Boozer's football career, entirely spent with the Jets, had ended, Clemons was telling Boozer about a musician he had met who was going to make him a lot of money. Clemons was an accomplished saxophone player, and he united with a little-known man named Bruce Springsteen in the 1970s. Before "The Boss" earned that nickname, Boozer saw Springsteen perform with Clemons, who would go on to become the most well-known face in the E Street Band.

3. Matt Snell holds a major grudge against the Jets organization, though no one is 100% sure about the origins of the tiff. The leading theory is that the Jets did not fulfill a

promise to hire him after his playing career was over, which upset the Jets legend enough that he cut off all contact with the team. When New York was attempting to honor him for his career in 2015, he refused to pick up the phone and he skipped out on the ceremony, in which the Jets also honored Emerson Boozer.

4. John Riggins and the Jets never really got along, and it was a major reason why Riggins ended up leaving New York to sign in Washington. He had a higher price tag to re-sign with the Jets—close to $450,000 per season—than he did for the rest of the league as Washington only paid Riggins $300,000 per season. After leaving, Riggins described the situation as a marriage that didn't work out due to broken promises and being undervalued by the franchise.

5. Freeman McNeil is perhaps best-known as the main plaintiff in the NFL Players Association's antitrust lawsuit against the NFL. McNeil and the NFLPA helped overturn the short-lived "Plan B" free agency instituted by the league and create the system that is currently in place today. McNeil didn't even benefit from the decision because he did not receive any money from the settlement, and he retired in 1992 before the changes were enacted into the league.

6. Johnny Hector played many different roles during his tenure with the Jets, on both offense and special teams. He was a kick returner early in his career while also serving

as a backup running back, then he formed the "Two-Headed Monster" with Freeman McNeil. He also made Jets history in 1986 as the first player to have both 100 yards rushing and 100 yards receiving in the same game. In that 14-13 win over Buffalo, Hector ran 18 times for 117 yards and caught nine passes for 100 yards.

7. Adrian Murrell's best day as a pro came almost 18 months before he was traded to the team he thrashed in 1996. Murrell ran for 199 yards on 31 carries in the Jets' only win of the 1996 season against the Arizona Cardinals in Phoenix. After the Jets acquired Curtis Martin, Murrell was expendable, and the Jets traded him to Arizona despite the fact he was just the second Jets player to have consecutive 1,000-yard seasons for the franchise.

8. The best season of Curtis Martin's career came the same year he dealt with a severe tear in his MCL for the second half of the season. He ran for nearly 1,700 yards in 2004 for the Jets, leading the league that year in yards and carries. However, he played with a Grade 3 tear in his MCL from the seventh game of the season onward, defying the suggestion from doctors that he needed surgery. He thought about sitting out the rest of the season and having surgery after receiving the news, but after talking with former Jets coach Bill Parcells, Martin decided to tough it out and he ended up having a career season.

9. Thomas Jones wasn't sure what he wanted to do after football. He had three 1,000-yard seasons in three years

with the Jets, but, after playing two years in Kansas City, he felt a bit stuck. He had started his own production company, and it was in one of those meetings with veteran actor Clifton Powell, he found his next project: acting. He is most known for his role of Comanche on Netflix's *Luke Cage*, though he has also appeared in the recent *Hawaii Five-O* reboot on CBS and the feature film *Straight Outta Compton*.

10. It might have taken a minor miracle for Chris Ivory to make it to the NFL, let alone to have a 1,000-yard season as he did in 2015 with the Jets. He was a fullback in high school who was recruited to college as a linebacker instead of a running back, but he ended up at Washington State, which believed in him as a running back. He was kicked off the team before his senior year due to disciplinary concerns around a second-degree assault charge that was later dropped and his oversleeping and missing a meeting. He ended his college career at Division II Tiffin, then was an undrafted free agent due to his perceived character flaws before he burst onto the scene with the Saints and set him up for a long career in the NFL.

CHAPTER 5:

CATCHING THE BALL

QUIZ TIME!

1. Which of these receivers had 500 catches in his career with the Jets?

    a. Al Toon
    b. Wesley Walker
    c. Laveranues Coles
    d. Mickey Shuler

2. How many yards did Don Maynard gain against Oakland in 1968 to set the Jets' single-game record for receiving yards?

    a. 217
    b. 221
    c. 228
    d. 233

3. Don Maynard caught the longest pass in Jets history.

    a. True
    b. False

4. Who holds the Jets' record for average yards per catch (minimum of 50 catches) with a staggering 19 yards per catch during his career in New York?

   a. Keyshawn Johnson
   b. Wesley Walker
   c. Brandon Marshall
   d. Don Maynard

5. Which pair of Jets became the team's first receiving duo to both exceed 1,000 yards in a season?

   a. Art Powell and Don Maynard
   b. Bake Turner and Don Maynard
   c. Don Maynard and George Sauer
   d. Al Toon and Wesley Walker

6. What is the Jets' record for most receiving touchdowns in a single season?

   a. 11
   b. 12
   c. 13
   d. 14

7. Don Maynard coined the term "wide receiver" to describe his playing style.

   a. True
   b. False

8. Mickey Shuler holds the Jets' record for receptions and receiving yards by a tight end, but who holds the franchise record for touchdown catches by a tight end, with 40?

a. Rich Caster

b. Anthony Becht

c. Jerome Barkum

d. Mickey Shuler

9. In which season did Mickey Shuler lead the Jets in receptions and receiving yards?

a. 1988

b. 1987

c. 1986

d. 1985

10. Who is the only Jets tight end to catch 10 or more touchdowns in the same season?

a. Anthony Becht

b. Rich Caster

c. Johnny Mitchell

d. Jerome Barkum

11. Which Jets receiver had a father who also worked in the Jets front office during his tenure as a player?

a. Wayne Chrebet

b. Robby Anderson

c. George Sauer

d. Al Toon

12. Art Powell is the only receiver to average 70 yards per game during his Jets career.

a. True

b. False

13. In which year did Wesley Walker lead the NFL in receiving yards and was named a First Team All-Pro?

    a. 1986
    b. 1983
    c. 1981
    d. 1978

14. For 27 years, Al Toon held the Jets' record for receptions in a season when he caught how many passes in 1988?

    a. 84
    b. 89
    c. 93
    d. 97

15. In which season did Keyshawn Johnson first record 1,000 receiving yards with the Jets?

    a. 1996
    b. 1997
    c. 1998
    d. 1999

16. How many times did Wayne Chrebet go over 1,000 yards in a season?

    a. 0
    b. 1
    c. 2
    d. 3

17. Which of these receivers caught 20 passes with the Jets during their time in New York?

a. Santonio Holmes

b. Santana Moss

c. Jerricho Cotchery

d. Robby Anderson

18. Laveranues Coles had more receiving yards in his second stint with the Jets than his first.

a. True

b. False

19. What is Brandon Marshall's franchise record for most receiving yards in a season?

a. 1,502

b. 1,494

c. 1,488

d. 1,476

20. How many times did Eric Decker and Brandon Marshall catch a touchdown in the same game to set the NFL record for teammates?

a. 10

b. 8

c. 11

d. 9

QUIZ ANSWERS

1. A – Al Toon

2. C – 228

3. B – False

4. B – Wesley Walker

5. A – Art Powell and Don Maynard

6. D – 14

7. A – True

8. C – Jerome Barkum

9. D – 1985

10. B – Rich Caster

11. C – George Sauer

12. B – False

13. D – 1978

14. C – 93

15. C – 1998

16. B – 1

17. D – Robby Anderson

18. A – True

19. A – 1,502

20. D – 9

DID YOU KNOW?

1. Don Maynard was the one who coined the term "wide receiver" to help explain to a reporter his role in the Jets' offense. The reporter wasn't sure if Maynard was a flanker or a split end, and Maynard explained that depending upon where he lined up in a given formation, he could be either. So he simply said that he was either the wide receiver on the left or the wide receiver on the right, and the name for the position stuck.

2. Art Powell put his career on the line several times to protest segregation and racial injustice during his playing days. He was cut by the Eagles after refusing to play in a preseason game for Philadelphia in 1960 when he learned he and his fellow black teammates would be housed in a different hotel from the rest of the team. He signed with the New York Titans and became a formidable duo with Don Maynard. However, he again refused to play in a preseason game for the same reasons with the Titans in 1961, and he was sold to Oakland the following year despite leading the AFL in receiving yards.

3. George Sauer Jr. is still all over the Jets' record book for his accomplishments on the field as a receiver, but his football talents weren't his true passion. His father, George Sauer Sr., was an accomplished player and later served as the Jets' director of player personnel for eight years. But while

Sauer was good at football, his passion was missing and many say he simply played the game because he didn't want to disappoint his father. The younger Sauer received a scholarship offer from the University of Texas the day he was born—and he did end up suiting up for the Longhorns—then was very productive in six years with the Jets before retiring at the age of 27. When leaving the sport, he criticized it for its "chauvinistic authority" and "militaristic structure" while also describing it as "inhumanly brutal."

4. Wesley Walker is legally blind in his left eye due to a congenital cataract but that didn't stop him from being one of the best receivers in Jets history. During his physical with the Jets after being drafted in 1977, the team discovered the vision in his right eye was 20/15, which is actually better than 20/20 vision. He had to make adjustments during games depending on the lighting, but he learned through his childhood how to use his peripheral vision and other tools to make himself successful on the gridiron.

5. The Jets drafted Mickey Shuler in 1978 intending to use him mainly as a blocker like he was at Penn State. By the time New York cut him in 1990, Shuler was the team's leader in receptions and receiving yards for a tight end— records he still holds today. In 12 years with the Jets, Shuler caught 438 passes for 4,819 yards and 37 touchdowns, and he led the team in receptions in 1984 and 1985 with 68 and 75 catches, respectively.

6. Al Toon took a pair of classes in college at the University of Wisconsin that paid big dividends for him on the field. While at Wisconsin, he took a ballet class to help with his flexibility and movement, and he studied tai chi to help him stay focused on the field. Those two classes were keys to keeping Toon nimble and graceful on the field as he was tearing up the NFL in his early seasons with the Jets before the injury bug hit him.

7. After his rookie season with the Jets, Keyshawn Johnson wrote a book with the help of reporter Shelley Smith about the 1996 season. The book created plenty of controversy around the team as Johnson was not too kind to several of his teammates and coaches in those pages. The book created a media firestorm around the team, though Bill Parcells and many other Jets players refused to comment on the book after its publication. It was part of many troubling incidents during Johnson's tenure with the team.

8. Wayne Chrebet was a bit surprised to hear from the Jets after the draft had concluded. He thought his mother had misremembered who was calling because his contact with the Bengals had a similar name to Jets coordinator of college scouting, John Griffin. As a Hofstra student, it was an easy walk for Chrebet from his dorm room to the workout with the Jets. He didn't drop a single pass during his workout and signed with the Jets for a $1,500 signing bonus. When he went to offseason workouts a few weeks later, he was stopped at the gate by security, who did not

believe he was a Jets player, and he was almost late to his first practice.

9. Laveranues Coles is a survivor of sexual abuse. Coles was molested by a man who would eventually become his stepfather, oftentimes at gunpoint, for three years from the ages of 10 to 13. The abuse was first revealed when Coles beat up a classmate for helping his stepfather spread a rumor that Coles was gay. His stepfather was sentenced to nine years in prison in 1992 for molesting Coles but served only three and a half years. Coles said that he used the anger and shame about the incident to help fuel him to become a Pro Bowl receiver once he began therapy and was able to channel his emotions into football.

10. In 2015, Eric Decker and Brandon Marshall tore up the NFL as the best receiver duo in the league that season. Marshall caught 109 passes for 1,502 yards and a league-leading 14 touchdowns, and Decker wasn't too far behind with 12 touchdown catches and 1,027 yards in their first season as a duo. Together, they set the NFL record by catching a touchdown in the same game nine times during the 2015 season to break the record set in 1998 by Randy Moss and Cris Carter in Minnesota.

CHAPTER 6:

TRENCH WARFARE

QUIZ TIME!

1. Who holds the Jets' record for most consecutive games played for the franchise at 195?

   a. Dan Alexander
   b. Randy Rasmussen
   c. Nick Mangold
   d. Winston Hill

2. Who was NOT part of the Jets' starting offensive line in Super Bowl III against the Colts?

   a. John Schmitt
   b. Randy Rasmussen
   c. Sam Walton
   d. Dave Herman

3. Who was the last Jets offensive lineman to be named to the Pro Bowl?

   a. Mekhi Becton
   b. Nick Mangold

c. Brandon Moore

d. D'Brickashaw Ferguson

4. The Jets have drafted just five offensive linemen in the 1st round since 1990.

a. True

b. False

5. What was Jumbo Elliott's actual first name?

a. Joshua

b. James

c. John

d. Jeremy

6. Though he played guard for the Jets, which position did Dan Alexander play at LSU?

a. Defensive tackle

b. Center

c. Offensive tackle

d. Linebacker

7. D'Brickashaw Ferguson played in every single snap possible of his NFL career.

a. True

b. False

8. How many times was Winston Hill named to the Pro Bowl, setting a Jets record?

a. 5

b. 6

c. 7

d. 8

9. Which Jets starting guard was the team's starting center in 2005 after Kevin Mawae was injured and then returned to guard in 2006 when the team drafted Nick Mangold?

    a. Jonathan Goodwin

    b. Dave Szott

    c. Pete Kendall

    d. Brandon Moore

10. Who is the only Jets offensive player to be named a First Team All-Pro three times?

    a. Jim Sweeney

    b. Marvin Powell

    c. Kevin Mawae

    d. Nick Mangold

11. Mark Gastineau set the single-game record for sacks in 1983 and tied it the following year with how many sacks?

    a. 3

    b. 3.5

    c. 4

    d. 4.5

12. Though it does not include his sacks from before 1982, Mark Gastineau still holds the Jets' team record for career sacks with how many?

    a. 74

    b. 77

c. 81

d. 83

13. Which defensive lineman was NOT part of the Jets' famed New York Sack Exchange defensive line of the 1980s?

a. Joe Klecko

b. Marty Lyons

c. Kenny Neil

d. Abdul Salaam

14. A Brooklyn police officer is credited with naming the Jets' defensive line the New York Sack Exchange.

a. True

b. False

15. What was Abdul Salaam's name during his rookie season with the Jets before he legally changed it?

a. Arnold Salem

b. Lorenzo Smith

c. Gerald Brown

d. Larry Faulk

16. Larry Grantham played both football and basketball during his time at Ole Miss.

a. True

b. False

17. Larry Grantham holds the Jets' record for most First Team All-Pro awards; he was named a First Team All-Pro how many times in the AFL?

a. 2

b. 3

c. 4

d. 5

18. Which of these Jets players did NOT register 50 sacks during his career in New York?

a. Calvin Pace

b. Shaun Ellis

c. Mo Lewis

d. John Abraham

19. Which Jets player collided with Dennis Byrd in 1992 that caused Byrd to break his neck and become paralyzed during a game against Kansas City?

a. Paul Frase

b. Mark Gunn

c. Kyle Clifton

d. Scott Mersereau

20. Which of these players was NOT named the Associated Press Defensive Rookie of the Year?

a. Shaun Ellis

b. Hugh Douglas

c. Sheldon Richardson

d. Jonathan Vilma

QUIZ ANSWERS

1. D – Winston Hill

2. C – Sam Walton

3. B – Nick Mangold

4. B – False

5. C – John

6. A – Defensive tackle

7. B – False

8. D – 8

9. C – Pete Kendall

10. B – Marvin Powell

11. C – 4

12. A – 74

13. C – Kenny Neil

14. A – True

15. D – Larry Faulk

16. B – False

17. D – 5

18. A – Calvin Pace

19. D – Scott Mersereau

20. A – Shaun Ellis

DID YOU KNOW?

1. Winston Hill holds the Jets' record for consecutive games played with 195 appearances from 1963 to 1976, a stretch that included 174 straight starts. During that time, he played through a broken leg in the preseason and was able to return to a 1974 game after having his throat stepped on. He was part of the Jets' inaugural Ring of Fame class in 2010 along with the man whose blindside he protected all of those seasons in New York, Joe Namath.

2. Randy Rasmussen accomplished the ultimate offensive lineman feat in 1972 by recovering a fumble for a touchdown. It was a power running play near the goal line where the two lines just mash into each other, trying to get the running back—Cliff McClain in this case—into the end zone. At the bottom of the pile, Rasmussen saw the ball drift through the bodies to the grass in front of him. He reached out and collected the fumble, then stretched it over the goal line and lay on top of it for the only score in his career.

3. Dan Alexander had played defensive tackle at LSU when he was drafted by the Jets in 1977. At his first practice, Alexander was told to line up with the offense and got into a fight during that first practice. Alexander ended up as the Jets' starting guard and played the next 153 games before his streak officially ended in 1987 due to the

players' strike. His unofficial streak lasted another season until a torn calf muscle ended it.

4. As poor as the Jets have been at times since winning the Super Bowl, they have always had stability at the center position. For 41 seasons from 1976 to 2016, New York had four centers start a combined 36 of those seasons—Joe Fields (1976-86), Jim Sweeney (1988-94), Kevin Mawae (1998-2005), and Nick Mangold (2007-16).

5. D'Brickashaw Ferguson played 10,707 of the 10,708 possible snaps during a 10-year career in which he started all 160 games. The one snap he missed came on the final play of the 2008 season when the Jets took him off the field to run a trick play in hopes of scoring a season-saving touchdown against Miami. If not for that missed snap, Ferguson would likely hold the NFL record for most consecutive snaps played, which was set by Joe Thomas with 10,363 snaps.

6. Larry Grantham's professional football career began, in a sense, on a baseball field in Mississippi. Grantham was overlooked by most colleges because of his size, but a Junior Legion baseball game in 1956 changed that perception. Future Hall-of-Famer Lance Alworth was on the opposing team, and he rounded third, trying to score on a bunt. Grantham was playing catcher, and, as Alworth charged toward home plate, he stood his ground to tag out the speedster. That day, the Ole Miss baseball coach signed him to a baseball scholarship and an assistant football

coach who was also at the game told Grantham to try out for the football team. His smaller stature never mattered on the field even though the heaviest Grantham weighed during his pro career was a measly 193 pounds.

7. Mark Gastineau headlined the vaunted New York Sack Exchange defensive line that taunted opposing quarterbacks in the 1980s. Gastineau, though, is probably just as well known for his actual taunting of opposing quarterbacks with his signature dance after each sack. His dances angered opponents and fans alike, and more than a few brawls were started because of the flamboyant nature of Gastineau's celebrations. He was just as outgoing off the field where he gathered headlines for his Rolls Royce and his engagement to actress Brigitte Nielsen.

8. Joe Klecko's omission from the Pro Football Hall of Fame is infuriating for many Jets fans and several media members who remember his production. As part of that famed New York Sack Exchange defensive front, Klecko was a four-time Pro Bowler and two-time First Team All-Pro lineman. In 1981, he unofficially led the league with 20.5 sacks, and he was the runaway AFC Defensive Player of the Year. His four Pro Bowl nods came at three different positions—defensive end, defensive tackle, and nose tackle—and he was as dominant as anyone on a team that never made much noise in the postseason.

9. Mo Lewis was a great player before Bill Parcells arrived in New York, but, under Parcells, Lewis blossomed into the

linebacker that dominated for the Jets. Lewis said Parcells tried to get under his skin a lot and goaded him into fights during practice, infusing the coach's combative nature into the players. It didn't mesh at first with Lewis's psyche, but, by the end of his first season under Parcells, he was the team's MVP. Then he was voted into three straight Pro Bowls and was an All-Pro selection in 1998.

10. John Abraham decided to play football as a senior in high school as a way to win a competition with his then-girlfriend. He and his girlfriend were competing to see who could earn the most accolades in the yearbook so he tried out for the football team, and, after just one season, he earned a scholarship offer from his home state school, the University of South Carolina. The Jets didn't talk with Abraham much when he was coming out of South Carolina, and they asked for much of his information just a day before the draft. Yet New York picked Abraham just moments after they drafted Shaun Ellis, who was with Abraham on draft day because they shared the same agent.

CHAPTER 7:

NO AIR ZONE

QUIZ TIME!

1. Who holds the Jets' record for most career interceptions?

   a. Bill Baird

   b. Aaron Glenn

   c. Darrelle Revis

   d. Victor Green

2. No Jets player has had 30 career interceptions with the franchise.

   a. True

   b. False

3. In which season did Dainard Paulson set the Jets' record with 12 interceptions?

   a. 1969

   b. 1967

   c. 1966

   d. 1964

4. Who was the first player in Jets history to have a 100-yard interception return?

    a. Marcus Coleman

    b. Erik McMillan

    c. Aaron Glenn

    d. Darrelle Revis

5. What is the Jets' record for most interceptions by a single player in a game?

    a. 6

    b. 5

    c. 4

    d. 3

6. How many touchdowns did Erik McMillan score to set the Jets' record for most defensive touchdowns in a career?

    a. 4

    b. 5

    c. 6

    d. 7

7. More than 200 players have intercepted a pass for the Jets.

    a. True

    b. False

8. Since 2008, who is the only player besides Darrelle Revis to have at least five interceptions in a season for the Jets?

    a. Jamal Adams

    b. Marcus Maye

c. Marcus Williams

d. Antonio Cromartie

9. Which of these defensive backs was NOT a multiple-time Pro Bowler with the Jets?

a. Jamal Adams

b. Bill Baird

c. Antonio Cromartie

d. Erik McMillan

10. In 1997, who set the Jets' record with three interception return touchdowns in a single season?

a. Ray Mickens

b. Otis Smith

c. Aaron Glenn

d. Victor Green

11. The Jets drafted Dainard Paulsen out of Oregon State as part of their original 1961 draft class.

a. True

b. False

12. What occupation was Bill Baird in before he got the call to try out for the NFL?

a. Cashier

b. Security guard

c. Janitor

d. Teacher

13. Burgess Owens had 21 interceptions in seven seasons as a member of the Jets. In 2020, he was elected to the US House of Representatives to represent which state?

a. Utah
b. New Jersey
c. Ohio
d. Colorado

14. Victor Green continued to increase on his interception numbers in seven straight years before topping out at six picks in which year?

a. 1998
b. 1999
c. 2000
d. 2001

15. In which year did Ty Law become the second Jets player ever to lead the league in interceptions?

a. 2003
b. 2004
c. 2005
d. 2006

16. In which season did Darrelle Revis NOT record at least five interceptions for the Jets?

a. 2008
b. 2009
c. 2011
d. 2015

17. In which year was Darrelle Revis NOT a First Team All-Pro cornerback for the Jets?

    a. 2011
    b. 2010
    c. 2009
    d. 2008

18. How long was Marcus Maye's interception return in 2018 against the Broncos that was the longest non-scoring interception return in NFL history?

    a. 102 yards
    b. 104 yards
    c. 106 yards
    d. 108 yards

19. Jamal Adams is the only other Jets defensive back besides Darrelle Revis to be named a First Team All-Pro.

    a. True
    b. False

20. How many interceptions did Jamal Adams have with the Jets?

    a. 2
    b. 3
    c. 4
    d. 5

QUIZ ANSWERS

1. A – Bill Baird

2. B – False

3. D – 1964

4. C – Aaron Glenn

5. D – 3

6. D – 7

7. A – True

8. C – Marcus Williams

9. B – Bill Baird

10. B – Otis Smith

11. B – False

12. D – Teacher

13. A – Utah

14. C – 2000

15. C – 2005

16. C – 2011

17. D – 2008

18. B – 104 yards

19. A – True

20. A – 2

DID YOU KNOW?

1. Dainard Paulson's love of football is the reason he became a member of the Jets. He was grateful for the chance to try out for the New York Titans in 1961 after going undrafted as a running back at Oregon State. He became a defensive back in New York, transitioning between safety and cornerback for his first few seasons. In 1964, he switched back to safety after having six interceptions as a cornerback and blossomed to set the franchise record with 12 interceptions in just 14 games.

2. Bill Baird's professional football career began with an innocent tryout on the football field at the high school where he was teaching. Baird was teaching at a San Francisco high school in 1962 after leading San Francisco State to the program's only unbeaten season three years earlier. The Baltimore Colts, coached by Weeb Ewbank, were in town to play the 49ers and were practicing at the high school where Baird taught. Baird's college coach asked the Colts to take a look at Baird, and they told him to report to training camp in 1963. He was cut on the last day of camp by the Colts, but then immediately picked up by the Jets, who had just signed Ewbank as their coach.

3. Darrol Ray was so not used to losing that he nearly gave himself an ulcer during his rookie year in New York. The Jets started the 1980 season 0-5, which was more losses

than Ray suffered during his three-year career at Oklahoma. Toward the end of November 1980, Ray would go to bed at 10:30 p.m., but wake up at 1:00 a.m. with chest pains and tightness in the middle of his chest. The Jets' doctors diagnosed him with a pre-ulcer condition and asked him if he felt responsible for the team's failures. That question seemed to cure all of Ray's worries as the pain went away after that conversation.

4. If Erik McMillan looked like a pro from the moment he stepped onto the field with the Jets, it makes sense. His father, Ernie McMillan, was a 15-year NFL veteran, and his cousin—Howard Richards—was a 1st round pick in 1981. That experience, plus his uncles who played professional basketball, prepared McMillan to be a professional athlete. And he produced like one immediately by leading the NFL with eight interceptions as a rookie in 1988 en route to being named the NFL Defensive Rookie of the Year and being voted to the first of two Pro Bowls.

5. Victor Green was coveted by roughly half of the NFL teams in 1993 as an undrafted free agent out of Akron. He ended up choosing the Jets because New York did not draft a defensive back that year. One of the reasons may have been the number of veteran free agents the Jets brought into camp, notably Ronnie Lott. Green and Lott built a tight bond during that 1993 season, as Lott would stay after practice to help Green with fundamentals and other necessary skills to be a safety in the NFL. That yearlong mentorship paid dividends for the Jets once

Green became a starter in 1995, a position he held for seven seasons.

6. James Hasty was a true competitor during his time in New York; though, sometimes, it got the better of him on the field. Several times during his tenure with the Jets, Hasty was seen yelling at teammates and expressing his frustration in the media about the Jets' failures. Though he was always apologetic about the outbursts, Hasty told the media at the end of the 1994 season that the emotions were simply the result of his frustrations with the constant losing. The *New York Times* described the response as a "goodbye speech" and that is exactly what it was because Hasty left the Jets that offseason.

7. Ray Mickens prided himself on being a solid cornerback both in the slot as a nickel back as well as an outside cornerback. Mickens played plenty of both during his tenure with the Jets, and, in an interview with the Jets' official website, he talked about how important that versatility was to him. "I wanted to make sure that I was versatile, that I could play inside and outside. I think that was one of the things that I realized about most of the guys in my position, they only wanted to play corner. They didn't like going into the slot. And some guys that played in the slot didn't like going outside as much. I have pride in embracing both and being good at both."

8. Aaron Glenn is responsible for two of the ten 100-plus-yard plays in Jets history. His first came in 1996 when he

intercepted a Dan Marino pass and returned it 100 yards for a touchdown. Two years later, he took a missed field goal 104 yards against the Colts.

9. Darrelle Revis's best season might be in 2009 when the lore of Revis Island firmly took hold. In 11 matchups against All-Pro and future Hall of Fame receivers, he allowed just one touchdown, and no receiver gained more than 55 yards or caught more than five passes. The following year, teams targeted him just 56 times, and he held Reggie Wayne to just one catch for a single yard in the Wild Card game against the Colts.

10. If it wasn't for George Adams's chipped pelvis giving him so much trouble later in life, Jamal Adams might not have been the hard-hitting safety he became in New York. When Jamal began playing football, George switched him to defense from running back to protect his son. He figured it would be easier on Jamal to be laying the ferocious hits at safety than receiving them at running back. He developed into one of the most feared safeties in the NFL and delivered some game-changing plays for the Jets during his time in New York.

CHAPTER 8:

SUPER BOWL SHUFFLE

QUIZ TIME!

1. The Jets were the first AFL team to win the Super Bowl.

   a. True
   b. False

2. Where was Super Bowl III played?

   a. Miami
   b. Pasadena
   c. Atlanta
   d. New Orleans

3. Who scored the Jets' only touchdown in Super Bowl III?

   a. Emerson Boozer
   b. Matt Snell
   c. George Sauer
   d. Joe Namath

4. How many times did the Jets intercept the Colts' quarterback tandem in their victory?

a. 2

b. 3

c. 4

d. 5

5. How many field goals did Jim Turner attempt in Super Bowl III?

    a. 4

    b. 6

    c. 3

    d. 5

6. Who led the Jets in receiving in Super Bowl III with eight catches for 133 yards?

    a. Matt Snell

    b. George Sauer

    c. Don Maynard

    d. Bill Mathis

7. How many yards did Matt Snell rush for in Super Bowl III?

    a. 104

    b. 113

    c. 121

    d. 132

8. The Jets scored points in all four quarters of Super Bowl III.

    a. True

    b. False

9. Who was named the MVP of Super Bowl III?

   a. Matt Snell
   b. Jim Turner
   c. Joe Namath
   d. Randy Beverly

10. How many points were the Colts favored by in Super Bowl III against the Jets?

   a. 12
   b. 14
   c. 16
   d. 18

11. How many wins did the 1968 Jets end with after capturing the franchise's only Lombardi Trophy?

   a. 11
   b. 12
   c. 13
   d. 14

12. The 16 points the Jets scored in Super Bowl III were the fewest they scored all season.

   a. True
   b. False

13. Which team defeated the Jets in the infamous "Heidi Game" that ended up being the Jets' final loss of the season?

   a. Miami Dolphins
   b. Buffalo Bills

c. Denver Broncos

d. Oakland Raiders

14. Which was the only team to beat the Jets in 1968 that New York was unable to exact revenge upon?

    a. Denver Broncos

    b. Oakland Raiders

    c. Houston Oilers

    d. Buffalo Bills

15. Which future NFL coaching legend was an assistant coach for the 1968 Jets?

    a. Buddy Ryan

    b. Bill Walsh

    c. Chuck Noll

    d. Bum Phillips

16. Who caught the game-winning touchdown pass in the AFL title game to send the Jets to Super Bowl III?

    a. Emerson Boozer

    b. George Sauer

    c. Matt Snell

    d. Don Maynard

17. What was the only year since the AFL-NFL merger that the Jets won the division and advanced to the conference championship game?

    a. 2010

    b. 2009

    c. 1998

    d. 1982

18. Which team has NOT defeated the Jets in the AFC Championship Game?

    a. Denver Broncos
    b. Indianapolis Colts
    c. Miami Dolphins
    d. New England Patriots

19. Which head coach did NOT lead the Jets to the AFC title game during his tenure?

    a. Joe Walton
    b. Walt Michaels
    c. Rex Ryan
    d. Bill Parcells

20. The Super Bowl has never been played at the Jets' home stadium.

    a. True
    b. False

QUIZ ANSWERS

1. A – True

2. A – Miami

3. B – Matt Snell

4. C – 4

5. D – 5

6. B – George Sauer

7. C – 121

8. B – False

9. C – Joe Namath

10. D – 18

11. C – 13

12. B – False

13. D – Oakland Raiders

14. A – Denver Broncos

15. A – Buddy Ryan

16. D – Don Maynard

17. C – 1998

18. D – New England Patriots

19. A – Joe Walton

20. B – False

DID YOU KNOW?

1. The Jets lost three games during the 1968 season, but none was as heartbreaking as the "Heidi Game." New York had taken a 32-29 lead over the Raiders with 1:05 left in the fourth quarter when the clock struck 7:00 p.m. on the East Coast. NBC, which was broadcasting the game that day, had scheduled the movie *Heidi* to begin at 7:00 p.m., and the network decided to cut away from the end of the game to begin the movie on time. Well, the Raiders scored 14 points in those final 65 seconds, and enough calls flooded the phone banks at NBC that the network publicly apologized for cutting away from the game.

2. Six weeks after the Heidi Game, the Jets and Raiders met again; this time, at Shea Stadium in the AFL Championship Game. New York led from the outset as Joe Namath hit Don Maynard for an early touchdown. The Jets didn't trail until late in the fourth quarter, but Namath had one final scoring drive in him. He marched the Jets down the field and found Maynard for a 5-yard touchdown to lift the Jets to a 27-23 win and a spot in Super Bowl III.

3. Joe Namath did a lot of talking in the lead-up to Super Bowl III, and he certainly did his part to back up his claims. He told the media that there were five AFL quarterbacks better than Earl Morrall, including Jets backup Babe Parilli, upsetting the Colts. However, Namath is most famous for

79

his guarantee on the Thursday before the Super Bowl when he was being honored as the Player of the Year. With a glass of Johnny Walker Red Label in his hand, Namath proclaimed to the audience that night in Miami, "We are going to win on Sunday. I guarantee it."

4. What does a coach tell his team before the biggest game of their lives? If you're Jets coach Weeb Ewbank, you tell a dirty joke. When asked by a reporter a year after the win what he told the team before Super Bowl III, Ewbank said, "I didn't know what to say. I thought we win. I thought we practiced well. I couldn't think of anything to say. So I told them a dirty joke."

5. Most people probably remember Super Bowl III as a battle between Joe Namath and Johnny Unitas, but that certainly was not the case. Unitas missed most of the season with torn muscles in his arm, and Earl Morrall stepped in and was the NFL MVP that season. However, Morrall was ineffective in the Super Bowl and was intercepted three times. By the time the Colts turned to Unitas in the fourth quarter, it was too late, despite Unitas leading Baltimore on its only scoring drive of the game. Unitas threw for 110 yards in the limited action while Morrall was held to just 71 passing yards.

6. Namath was named the Super Bowl MVP despite not throwing a touchdown pass. He was efficient as a passer, completing 17 of 28 attempts for 206 yards, but the award could have easily also gone to Matt Snell. The Jets running back had 30 carries for 121 yards and New York's only

touchdown, which put the Jets up 7-0 early in the game. It could also have been Jim Turner, who made three of his five field goal attempts and led the game in scoring with nine points.

7. The coaching matchup of Super Bowl III was tantalizing with Don Shula facing off against Weeb Ewbank. Shula famously replaced Ewbank as the Colts' head coach after Ewbank led Baltimore to two NFL titles in the late 1950s. But there were two key assistant coaches in the game as well. The Jets' defensive line was coached by Buddy Ryan, who would later become the architect of the Bears' 1985 defense. On the opposing sideline, the Colts' defensive coordinator was Chuck Noll, who would go on to become a Hall of Fame coach with the Steelers shortly after Baltimore's stunning loss to the Jets.

8. John Schmitt overcame a serious bout of pneumonia to play in Super Bowl III for the Jets. The center started to feel ill after the AFL Championship win over the Raiders, and the team doctors refused to administer penicillin, thinking he was allergic to the medicine. In the two weeks leading up to the Super Bowl, Schmitt was coughing up blood and phlegm but continued to practice at his coach's behest to not tip off the fact he was sick. Just days before the game, Schmitt gave the ultimatum to give him penicillin or he wouldn't be able to play. Schmitt went on to start and play the entire game, though he noted that he was slower getting to the line of scrimmage as the game progressed due to the effects of his illness.

9. The championship ring is one of the most iconic pieces of jewelry on the planet, and the Jets almost didn't receive rings for their win over Baltimore. Weeb Ewbank preferred to gift his players watches instead of rings, but the players' committee, led by Joe Namath, persuaded the coach to get the rings instead. They're understated by today's metrics with 14 karat gold and two carats worth of diamonds, and more important, they are the first rings to feature the words "Super Bowl" on them.

10. The Jets' Super Bowl rings have been lost and found in some strange places over the years. John Schmitt lost his in Hawaii in 1971, and it was returned to him 40 years later by the family of a lifeguard who found it while snorkeling in 1971. Emerson Boozer's cat stole his ring once and hid it behind the furnace, while Randy Rasmussen dropped his on a golf course, and it was returned to him four years later when it was found in the dirt. Perhaps the strangest, though, is Don Maynard, who stored his ring in the refrigerator for safekeeping because it wouldn't be burned down in a fire nor stolen by any would-be burglars.

CHAPTER 9:

SHINING THE BUSTS

QUIZ TIME!

1. Which of these future Hall-of-Famers was NOT drafted by the Jets?

    a. Joe Namath
    b. Mel Renfro
    c. John Mackey
    d. Herb Adderley

2. How many people with ties to the Jets organization will be enshrined in the Hall of Fame by the end of 2021?

    a. 14
    b. 16
    c. 18
    d. 20

3. No Jets Hall-of-Famer played his entire career with the team.

    a. True
    b. False

4. Who was the first Jets player enshrined in the Hall of Fame?

   a. Winston Hill
   b. Joe Namath
   c. John Riggins
   d. Weeb Ewbank

5. Which of these Hall-of-Famers played multiple years for the Jets?

   a. Steve Atwater
   b. LaDainian Tomlinson
   c. Jason Taylor
   d. Ed Reed

6. How many of the Jets' Hall-of-Famers were in some way connected to the team's 1968 Super Bowl championship?

   a. 4
   b. 5
   c. 6
   d. 7

7. Which Hall-of-Famer did NOT end his career with the Jets?

   a. Steve Atwater
   b. LaDainian Tomlinson
   c. Ronnie Lott
   d. Alan Faneca

8. Joe Namath is the only Hall-of-Famer the Jets drafted who played for the team.

a. True

b. False

9. Which NFL franchise did Don Maynard start his career with in 1958 before moving to Canada and eventually winding up with the Jets?

a. San Francisco 49ers

b. Dallas Cowboys

c. New York Giants

d. Green Bay Packers

10. Which team signed both Winston Hill and Joe Namath in 1977 after both Jets legends were let go by the team?

a. Los Angeles Rams

b. Oakland Raiders

c. San Francisco 49ers

d. St. Louis Cardinals

11. John Riggins set his career high for rushing yards in a game while with the Jets. How many yards did he rush for on that day in 1972 against New England?

a. 159

b. 162

c. 168

d. 174

12. How old was Weeb Ewbank when he took over the Jets in 1963?

a. 53

b. 56

c. 59

d. 62

13. Which team drafted Kevin Mawae in 1994 before the center left in free agency to join the Jets?

   a. Houston Oilers

   b. Minnesota Vikings

   c. Seattle Seahawks

   d. Cleveland Browns

14. Curtis Martin rushed for 1,000 yards every season he played for the Jets.

   a. True

   b. False

15. How many sacks did Jason Taylor record during his career with the Jets?

   a. 2

   b. 3.5

   c. 5

   d. 6

16. How many passes did Art Monk catch during his only season with the Jets in 1994?

   a. 37

   b. 39

   c. 43

   d. 46

17. How many times did Brett Favre throw for 300 yards in a game during his one year with the Jets in 2008?

a. 0

b. 1

c. 2

d. 4

18. Ronnie Lott and Ed Reed both had the same number of interceptions during their brief stints with the Jets. How many picks did each have?

a. 6

b. 5

c. 4

d. 3

19. Ty Law set his career high in interceptions in a single season with the Jets.

a. True

b. False

20. Which Hall-of-Famer most recently played on the Jets?

a. Alan Faneca

b. Ed Reed

c. Jason Taylor

d. LaDainian Tomlinson

QUIZ ANSWERS

1. B – Mel Renfro

2. C – 18

3. A – True

4. B – Joe Namath

5. B – LaDainian Tomlinson

6. A – 4

7. D – Alan Faneca

8. B – False

9. C – New York Giants

10. A – Los Angeles Rams

11. C – 168

12. B – 56

13. C – Seattle Seahawks

14. B – False

15. C – 5

16. D – 46

17. A – 0

18. D – 3

19. A – True

20. D – LaDainian Tomlinson

DID YOU KNOW?

1. Weeb Ewbank is the only coach ever to win a title in both the NFL and the AFL. He was on the winning side of two of the most famous games in NFL history. Ewbank coached the Baltimore Colts to a thrilling overtime win over the New York Giants for the first of two straight NFL titles in 1958 in what is considered the greatest game ever played. He then led the Jets over the Colts in Super Bowl III for arguably the greatest upset in Super Bowl history. He finished his coaching career with a modest record of 134 wins, 130 losses, and seven ties.

2. As football has evolved over the years, there have been several analytics-based opinions that Joe Namath should not be in the Hall of Fame. What most people cite is that Namath had a losing record as a starter—60-61-4 as the Jets' starter in 12 years—and his completion percentage was barely above 50%. He threw more interceptions than touchdown passes, and he didn't even average 200 yards per game with the Jets. However, there are more nuanced stats that point to Namath's Hall of Fame credentials as does his leadership and confidence that made the Jets competitive for the most part during his prime.

3. When Don Maynard retired in 1973, he had written the record book for receivers in the NFL. At the time of his retirement, Maynard was the league's all-time leading receiver with 633 catches and 11,834 yards, and he made

an instant impact with the New York Titans in 1960. He caught a career-best 72 passes that year and had the first of five 1,000-yard seasons with the Jets. In 1967, Maynard came a reception short of tying his career high in catches but led the league with 1,434 yards, which was his career high.

4. Despite being an All-Pro in Washington in 1983, John Riggins's only Pro Bowl appearance came in his final year with the Jets. He became the first Jets running back to rush for 1,000 yards when he rumbled for 1,005 yards. Riggins also caught 30 passes for more than 350 yards, though the Jets won just three games that season. Riggins was a character during his time in New York with some wild hairstyles that included an afro and a mohawk that formed an arrow down his scalp. Joe Namath even said he saw Riggins paint his toenails green before a game once while with the Jets.

5. Curtis Martin has a very interesting relationship with football, the sport that earned him so many accolades. During his enshrinement speech, Martin described not being a football fan and never really watching the game much, especially not entire games growing up or in retirement. Even after he was drafted by New England, his first reaction was to tell his family that he wasn't sure if he wanted to play professional football. What changed his mind, though, was his pastor who told him that football might be the avenue God chose for him to spread the messages he wanted to spread in the world. That

became his connection to football and fueled his passion for his career.

6. Kevin Mawae was right-handed for most of his career, but not for five weeks in 2004. On a simple screen pass against the Chargers in Week 2, Mawae got the fingers on his right hand tangled in the facemask of the linebacker he was blocking, causing them to bend at weird angles. He was diagnosed with a fractured metacarpal, but it didn't deter him from continuing his consecutive games played streak. After a fortuitous Week 3 bye, Mawae played the next five games left-handed and helped New York begin the season 6-1.

7. Winston Hill unfortunately died in 2016, four years before he was inducted into the Hall of Fame as part of the museum's Centennial Celebration that included an expanded class of inductees. Many people assumed Hill's prowess would be forgotten to history because he was never a finalist for the Modern-Era or Senior Committees, but he was voted into the Hall of Fame in 2020 and was enshrined in a rescheduled ceremony in 2021. Fellow Hall-of-Famer Joe Namath told the Jets' official website in 2019 that Hill should be in the Hall of Fame, saying "what made Winston Hill one of the best offensive linemen ever to play was his ability to execute and protect the quarterback and block for the running game. If you look at one game, the Super Bowl, you see Matt Snell running that ball so many times behind Winston. Without Winston Hill that day—we don't win the championship."

8. There are so many stories around the legendary Bill Parcells, but the most mysterious are his name and his nickname. He was born Duane Charles Parcells, but his classmates in elementary school confused him with another kid, whose name was Bill, and the nickname stuck with him. In his first year as an assistant coach, Parcells yelled at a player he thought was loafing during practice. He asked the player, "Who do you think I am? Charlie Tuna?" From that, he earned the nickname "Tuna," which adjusted to "Big Tuna" when he started to have success while coaching the Giants.

9. The Jets have seven Hall-of-Famers who made a major contribution to the franchise during their Hall of Fame careers as defined by the Pro Football Hall of Fame. Bill Parcells is the most famous of the bunch who is not included on that list, which also includes Alan Faneca, Ronnie Lott, LaDainian Tomlinson, and Ron Wolf, who spent multiple years with the Jets. Steve Atwater, Brett Favre, Art Monk, Ed Reed, and Jason Taylor all played one season in New York during their Hall of Fame careers, and Ty Law had a pair of one-season stints with the Jets.

10. The next former Jets player to be inducted into the Hall of Fame might take a while. Alan Faneca earned his gold jacket in the class of 2021, and he was the only former Jets player named as a semifinalist for induction. Among those who were on the original list of 130 nominees published by the Hall of Fame were John Abraham and

D'Brickashaw Ferguson, both of whom may eventually earn their way to Canton.

CHAPTER 10:

DRAFT DAY

QUIZ TIME!

1. Which future Hall-of-Famer did the Jets select in their first draft in 1961, although he never played for the team?

    a. John Mackey

    b. Bob Lilly

    c. Jimmy Johnson

    d. Herb Adderley

2. Which Super Bowl hero did the Jets draft with the 3rd overall pick in the 1964 AFL Draft?

    a. Randy Beverly

    b. George Sauer

    c. Matt Snell

    d. Jim Turner

3. In which round of the 1966 Draft did the Jets select Emerson Boozer?

    a. 8th

    b. 7th

c. 6th

d. 5th

4. The Jets have picked 1st overall more times than they have picked 2nd overall.

   a. True

   b. False

5. With which pick in the 1st round did the Jets draft John Riggins in 1971?

   a. 6th

   b. 9th

   c. 13th

   d. 15th

6. The 1977 Draft provided the Jets with some excellent talent that would come to define the team during the 1980s. Who was not part of that draft class?

   a. Joe Klecko

   b. Mickey Shuler

   c. Wesley Walker

   d. Dan Alexander

7. The same year the Jets drafted Mark Gastineau in the 2nd round, they used their 1st round pick on another defensive end.

   a. True

   b. False

8. What pick number did the Jets hold in 1983 when they drafted Ken O'Brien as the fifth quarterback in that iconic class?

    a. 18th
    b. 21st
    c. 23rd
    d. 24th

9. In 1984, the Jets used their 3rd round selection to draft which linebacker?

    a. Kyle Clifton
    b. Rusty Guilbeau
    c. Lance Mehl
    d. Harry Hamilton

10. In which round of the 1988 Draft did the Jets draft James Hasty out of Washington State?

    a. 5th
    b. 3rd
    c. 6th
    d. 4th

11. Which quarterback did the Jets draft in the 2nd round of the 1991 NFL Draft, one round before they took Mo Lewis?

    a. Jeff Blake
    b. Paul Justin
    c. Browning Nagle
    d. Troy Taylor

12. Who was New York's first 1st round pick in 1995 before Hugh Douglas became its second 1st round choice that year?

   a. Ryan Yarborough
   b. Aaron Glenn
   c. Marvin Jones
   d. Kyle Brady

13. Keyshawn Johnson is the only 1st overall draft pick in Jets history.

   a. True
   b. False

14. Who did the Jets end up drafting in the 1st round in 1997 after trading down from both 1st and 6th overall?

   a. Alex Van Dyke
   b. Walter Jones
   c. Rick Terry
   d. James Farrior

15. The Jets famously had four 1st round picks in 2000; who did they choose with their assigned 1st round pick that year?

   a. Shaun Ellis
   b. Anthony Becht
   c. John Abraham
   d. Chad Pennington

16. Mike Nugent was the first player the Jets drafted in 2005.

   a. True
   b. False

17. How many picks did the Jets make in 2009, the fewest the franchise has ever made in a single draft?

    a. 2
    b. 3
    c. 4
    d. 5

18. Who was the last Jets 1st round selection to be picked outside the top 10?

    a. Mekhi Becton
    b. Calvin Pryor
    c. Darron Lee
    d. Leonard Williams

19. When was the last time the Jets did NOT make a selection in the 1st round?

    a. 2012
    b. 2008
    c. 2005
    d. 2002

20. Which Jets draft pick has played the most games in the NFL?

    a. James Farrior
    b. Terance Mathis
    c. Craig Hentrich
    d. Jim Sweeney

QUIZ ANSWERS

1. D – Herb Adderley

2. C – Matt Snell

3. C – 6th

4. B – False

5. A – 6th

6. B – Mickey Shuler

7. A – True

8. D – 24th

9. A – Kyle Clifton

10. B – 3rd

11. C – Browning Nagle

12. D – Kyle Brady

13. B – False

14. D – James Farrior

15. D – Chad Pennington

16. A – True

17. B – 3

18. A – Mekhi Becton

19. C – 2005

20. C – Craig Hentrich

DID YOU KNOW?

1. The race for Joe Namath's signature after the 1965 AFL and NFL Drafts was one of the first truly fair arms races. The AFL was infused with cash from its television deal with NBC, so AFL teams were able to offer better compensation for the prospects than previously. When the Cardinals drafted Namath with the 12th overall pick, Namath demanded a contract for $200,000 per year and a Lincoln Continental convertible. The Cardinals balked at the request initially but agreed to the terms as long as Namath signed before the Orange Bowl. Instead, Namath signed a three-year, $427,000 deal with the Jets immediately after leading Alabama to a win in the Orange Bowl, a contract that included a new car and employment for his siblings.

2. Emerson Boozer had a tough decision to make in 1966 after being drafted by both the Jets and Steelers. Boozer decided to sign with the Jets because he saw Joe Namath play on television while Namath was playing at Alabama. He also saw Matt Snell play at Ohio State and George Sauer play at Texas. Boozer explained, "You want to play with some of these guys that you've seen and that you know about. I figured we could probably form a pretty good group. And we did. The choice was the right choice."

3. Entering the 1971 NFL Draft, there were questions about whether or not John Riggins or Ohio State's John

Brockington was the best running back in the draft. Riggins had an excellent career at Kansas and had all the physical tools to be successful, but there was one downside most scouts noted—his attitude. Riggins was asked by scouts to do the same tests repeatedly and that frustrated Riggins at times, and his complaints were seen as indicating a poor attitude. However, the Jets were not scared off by the eccentricities and decided to draft Riggins with the 6th pick in 1971.

4. Ken O'Brien was literally in bed when the Jets drafted him in 1983. As a senior at the University of California-Davis, O'Brien was far more concerned with his Spanish exam later that day than with the draft. It wasn't until Jets coach Joe Walton called him at 8:00 a.m. Pacific that O'Brien even learned that New York had picked him. He woke up his roommates to let them know the news and then called his parents to celebrate before he biked over to his Spanish exam across campus.

5. If it weren't for his thigh bone being too hollow, Mo Lewis wouldn't have been drafted by the Jets. The Cleveland Browns were very interested in the linebacker coming out of the University of Georgia, but the discovery of his thigh problem ended their pursuit of Lewis. On the day of the draft, Lewis didn't even know it was happening until he got a call from Dick Steinberg saying the Jets had drafted him. Lewis actually hung up the phone, assuming it was a prank, but after Steinberg called back, Lewis realized he

had been drafted and then started learning about the Jets, who had never really shown much interest in him before.

6. Ray Mickens was a little disappointed to be drafted by the Jets with the 1st pick in the 3rd round. It wasn't that he was upset to be going to the Jets, but, as an All-American at Texas A&M, he expected to be a 1st round pick, and, if not, he would definitely be drafted in the 2nd round. Chicago and Miami were among the five teams that had told Mickens they would be very interested in drafting him in the 2nd round, but the phone never rang. When the television broadcast went to commercial after the final pick of the 2nd round, Mickens was upset not to be drafted, but the frustration was short-lived, as he also received the call from the Jets that they had drafted him.

7. The New York Jets took nearly eight minutes to debate whether or not to draft Chad Pennington with the 18th overall pick in 2000. Much of that discussion was due to Denver and San Francisco trying to trade back into the 1st round to draft Pennington, but no deal was satisfactory to New York's front office. If the Jets hadn't drafted Pennington, the Marshall quarterback likely would have gone 19th to the Seahawks, whose representative in New York was exasperated when the Jets' selection was announced.

8. The Jets set an NFL record by making four picks in the 1st round of the 2000 NFL Draft. Not only did they make those four picks, but all of them became impact players in

the NFL and played at least 11 seasons in the league. New York made its first pick at 12th overall by drafting Shaun Ellis, then immediately followed up by drafting John Abraham with the 13th pick. Five picks later, the Jets used their own 1st round pick to select Pennington and then rounded out the stellar 1st round class by drafting Anthony Becht at 27th overall. Four different Jets coaches had at least one of the four players drafted in the 1st round in 2000 on their team during their tenure.

9. While many fans had hoped the Jets would draft a quarterback in 2006 with the 4th overall pick, the franchise had a different plan in mind. New York had two 1st round picks that year, thanks to having traded John Abraham to Atlanta, and the Jets used both of them on the offensive line. They drafted D'Brickashaw Ferguson at 4th overall, then came back later and drafted Nick Mangold. Both of them made a big impact on the line during their time with the Jets. Eric Mangini told the *New York Post* in 2020 that he told his scouts and coaches before the draft, "I don't care if John Elway was in this draft, we can't block [New England's] Richard Seymour, we can't block [Miami's] Jason Taylor, so if we don't help anybody up front, whether it's Chad Pennington or whomever, nothing matters, we can all go home right now. We stink on the offensive line."

10. Throughout the pre-draft process ahead of the 2018 NFL Draft, Mike Maccagnan assumed he wouldn't be able to draft Sam Darnold. The Jets had been at every one of his

games in 2017, and they fell in love with his personality during the interviews and meetings they had with Darnold. But the assumption was that Darnold would be drafted by Cleveland with the 1st overall pick. So when the Browns drafted Baker Mayfield instead, and the Giants decided not to draft a quarterback, Maccagnan was impatient to put in the draft card with Darnold's name on it. He was forced to wait by the NFL for television purposes, so Maccagnan walked around the room a bit before the league finally let the Jets officially draft Darnold.

CHAPTER 11:

LET'S MAKE A DEAL!

QUIZ TIME!

1. Which team traded the 1ˢᵗ overall pick in the 1965 Draft to the Jets in order for New York to draft Joe Namath?

    a. Houston Oilers

    b. Kansas City Chiefs

    c. Denver Broncos

    d. Buffalo Bills

2. With which team did the Jets trade in 1980 to move up in the draft to select Johnny "Lam" Jones?

    a. Green Bay Packers

    b. Arizona Cardinals

    c. Minnesota Vikings

    d. San Francisco 49ers

3. The Jets traded a pair of draft choices in 1984 to move up in the draft to pick Jim Sweeney.

    a. True

    b. False

4. To which team did the Jets send Richard Todd in 1984?

    a. Seattle Seahawks
    b. Tampa Bay Buccaneers
    c. New Orleans Saints
    d. Kansas City Chiefs

5. In which round was the draft pick that the Jets sent the Bengals in exchange for Boomer Esiason?

    a. 6th
    b. 5th
    c. 4th
    d. 3rd

6. Where did the Jets ship Ken O'Brien after acquiring Boomer Esiason from Cincinnati?

    a. Arizona Cardinals
    b. Green Bay Packers
    c. Philadelphia Eagles
    d. Tampa Bay Buccaneers

7. In which year was the 1st round pick the Jets sent to New England to hire Bill Parcells as head coach?

    a. 1997
    b. 1998
    c. 1999
    d. 2000

8. Which 1st round pick did the Jets trade to San Francisco to move up and draft Shaun Ellis?

a. Pick acquired in Bill Belichick trade

b. Lower pick acquired in Keyshawn Johnson trade

c. Higher pick acquired in Keyshawn Johnson trade

d. Own pick

9. Who was the player the Jets acquired when they traded Santana Moss to Washington in 2005?

a. Leon Washington

b. Justin McCareins

c. Laveranues Coles

d. Jerricho Cotchery

10. The Jets traded up with the Carolina Panthers to draft Darrelle Revis in 2007.

a. True

b. False

11. Which team did the Jets trade with to move up in the 2009 Draft to pick Mark Sanchez?

a. Jacksonville Jaguars

b. Cleveland Browns

c. Cincinnati Bengals

d. Kansas City Chiefs

12. Which two draft picks did the Jets give up before the 2010 Draft to acquire Santonio Holmes from the Steelers and Antonio Cromartie from the Chargers?

a. 2010 5th and 2011 2nd

b. 2010 6th and 2011 2nd

c. 2010 5th and 2011 3rd

d. 2010 6th and 2011 3rd

13. Which was NOT one of the picks involved in the Jets' trade for Tim Tebow in 2012?

    a. 2012 Jets 4th round pick
    b. 2012 Jets 6th round pick
    c. 2012 Broncos 7th round pick
    d. 2012 Jets 7th round pick

14. The Jets packaged the 1st round pick they acquired in the Darrelle Revis trade to move up in the first round of the 2013 NFL Draft.

    a. True
    b. False

15. Which wide receiver did the Jets acquire in exchange for their 6th round pick in the 2015 NFL Draft?

    a. Eric Decker
    b. Brandon Marshall
    c. DeVier Posey
    d. Percy Harvin

16. In which round was the draft pick the Jets surrendered to Houston to trade for Ryan Fitzpatrick in 2015?

    a. 4th
    b. 5th
    c. 6th
    d. 7th

17. Which pick number was the 1st round pick the Jets sent the Colts as part of the trade to move up to draft Sam Darnold in 2018?

a. 5th

b. 6th

c. 7th

d. 8th

18. In which round was the draft pick the Jets acquired when they traded Teddy Bridgewater to the Saints before the 2018 season?

a. 5th

b. 4th

c. 3rd

d. 2nd

19. Which player did the Jets acquire along with three draft picks when they traded Jamal Adams to Seattle?

a. Quincy Wilson

b. Ashtyn Davis

c. Pierre Desir

d. Bradley McDougald

20. The Jets made three trades during the 2020 regular season.

a. True

b. False

QUIZ ANSWERS

1. A – Houston Oilers

2. D – San Francisco 49ers

3. B – False

4. C – New Orleans Saints

5. D – 3rd

6. B – Green Bay Packers

7. C – 1999

8. A – Pick acquired in Bill Belichick trade

9. C – Laveranues Coles

10. A – True

11. B – Cleveland Browns

12. A – 2010 5th and 2011 2nd

13. D – 2012 Jets 7th round pick

14. B – False

15. D – Percy Harvin

16. C – 6th

17. B – 6th

18. C – 3rd

19. D – Bradley McDougald

20. A – True

DID YOU KNOW?

1. The Houston Oilers originally held the 1st overall pick in the 1965 AFL Draft. However, the Jets traded to Houston the rights to negotiate with quarterback Jerry Rhome for the first selection. New York used that pick to select Joe Namath out of Alabama. The Jets then tried to orchestrate a trade with the Rams to send Namath to Los Angeles per his wishes, but a deal could never be struck, so the Jets waived him.

2. The Jets' trade for Boomer Esiason in 1993 might have had as much to do with wooing free agent Reggie White as trying to upgrade the quarterback position. When White visited the Jets as a free agent, he told the franchise that he was more likely to sign with the Jets if they traded for Esiason. Within 24 hours, New York had completed the trade for a 3rd round pick, and a few weeks later, the Jets sent Ken O'Brien to the Packers for a draft choice. The timing was likely coincidental since both the Bengals and Jets said the trade was nearing completion before White's visit, but it didn't matter anyway because White signed with the Packers.

3. When Bill Parcells took over the Jets in 1997, the franchise had a chance to draft a future Hall-of-Famer in Orlando Pace with the 1st overall pick. Instead, Parcells wanted to acquire a lot of draft picks, so he traded the number one

pick to the Rams for the 6th overall pick as well as picks in the 3rd, 4th, and 6th rounds. Parcells didn't even keep the 6th pick, trading it to Tampa Bay for the 8th pick as well as a 4th round selection in 1997. The Buccaneers then traded the pick to Seattle, who drafted future Hall-of-Famer Walter Jones with the pick, and the Jets drafted James Farrior with the 8th pick.

4. The Jets' rebuild through the 2000 Draft came at the cost of Bill Belichick and Keyshawn Johnson. Belichick was in a legal battle with the Jets over whether or not he could interview, and then accept, the head coaching position with the Patriots despite technically being the Jets' head coach. The contentious relationship ended with New England sending the Jets a 1st round pick in 2000 as well as 4th and 7th round picks in 2001 in exchange for Belichick and two draft picks. Later that offseason, the Jets called Johnson's bluff and shipped the disgruntled receiver to Tampa Bay for two 1st round picks in 2000.

5. After leaving the Jets in free agency in 2003, Laveranues Coles was very happy for a reunion with his former franchise in 2005. It was a rare case of both sides being happy because New York was able to unload disgruntled receiver Santana Moss in exchange for Coles, who had demanded a trade from Washington during the 2005 offseason. The trade took nearly a month to complete as the two teams started and stopped negotiations several times between the scouting combine in February and the deal being completed in March.

6. The process to acquire Brett Favre from the Packers was a long one for Jets general manager Mike Tannenbaum. Through the three-week saga, the trade seemed dead numerous times, and there was a mystery text message that ended up securing Favre in New York. The Jets first had to convince Favre to come play for the team after he expressed hesitancy about playing in the New York market. The text message Tannenbaum sent to ownership, Coach Eric Mangini, and other high-ranking officials said: "I have great F---ING NEWS! CALL ME! GREAT NEWS!!!!!!!!!!!" with 11 exclamation points after "great news." The Jets only had to surrender a 3rd round pick to secure Favre's services after an ugly divorce in Green Bay.

7. Darrelle Revis was coming off knee surgery in 2013 when the Jets traded him to Tampa Bay for the Buccaneers' 1st round pick in 2013 and a 2014 3rd round pick (that reverted to a 4th round pick when Tampa Bay cut him after the 2013 season). New York and Tampa Bay had agreed to the terms of the trade, but the final hurdle was what the Buccaneers' doctors thought of Revis's knee. He passed the physical with flying colors, completing a deal that had seemed destined to fail when the Jets asked for three draft picks and the Buccaneers drawing the line at two. Tampa Bay even set a deadline for New York to agree to a deal or the Buccaneers would pull out of negotiations.

8. When the Jets decided to trade for Brandon Marshall in 2015, they did so with plenty of intel on the receiver they

were acquiring. Jets Coach Todd Bowles was on the coaching staff in Miami for the two years that Marshall played with the Dolphins in 2010 and 2011. The Jets director of college scouting was a former Bears scout who was familiar with Marshall from his time in Chicago. The Jets also hired Karl Dorrell as their receiver coach, reuniting Marshall with his position coach from Miami.

9. The Jets had two plans heading into the 2018 Draft process: sign Kirk Cousins or trade up in the draft. After failing to sign Cousins, the Jets turned their attention to trying to move up from the 6th overall pick. Any trade with Cleveland at 1st overall was going to cost too much, and the Jets never even tried to call the Giants for fear of the price being so high because they share the same market. So the Jets focused on Indianapolis at number three, and the first conversations about a trade came during the Senior Bowl in January when Jets Vice President of Player Personnel Brian Heimerdinger spoke to his Colts counterpart, Ed Dodds. The two men left their meeting that day with an agreement to keep talking, and they kept in contact until mid-March when the actual trade talks began in earnest. Within a week, the deal was done, and the Jets had moved up to 3rd overall in the draft, where they picked Sam Darnold.

10. Throughout the pandemic-affected offseason in 2020, Jamal Adams was asking for a trade from the Jets in a pretty public forum. He had wanted to restructure his rookie contract, and, when that failed, he criticized Jets

114

ownership as well as Coach Adam Gase in the week leading up to his eventual trade. New York was adamant about not trading Adams, though they did listen to offers at the trade deadline in 2019, which angered Adams. Ultimately, the offer from Seattle was too good to ignore, and the Jets shipped Adams west for two 1st round picks—one in 2021 and one in 2022—as well as a 2021 3rd round pick and Bradley McDougald.

CHAPTER 12:

WRITING THE RECORD BOOK

QUIZ TIME!

1. What is the Jets' record for most passing yards in a game, set by Joe Namath in 1972?

    a. 482

    b. 496

    c. 503

    d. 514

2. Who is the only quarterback besides Joe Namath to throw for 20,000 yards with the Jets?

    a. Sam Darnold

    b. Richard Todd

    c. Chad Pennington

    d. Ken O'Brien

3. Who holds the Jets' record for leading most game-winning drives in a career?

    a. Joe Namath

    b. Vinny Testaverde

c. Ken O'Brien

d. Chad Pennington

4. How many interceptions did Al Dorow and Richard Todd throw to tie for the team's single-season record?

   a. 25

   b. 27

   c. 30

   d. 31

5. Curtis Martin has 2,000 more yards in his Jets career than the franchise's second-place rusher.

   a. True

   b. False

6. Who has the second-most rushing touchdowns in Jets history, with 52?

   a. Emerson Boozer

   b. Johnny Hector

   c. Curtis Martin

   d. Freeman McNeil

7. What is the record for most carries by a Jets running back in a season?

   a. 362

   b. 368

   c. 371

   d. 377

8. Curtis Martin holds the Jets' record for rushing touchdowns in a single season.

a. True

b. False

9. Don Maynard holds the Jets' record for career total touchdowns, with how many?

   a. 69

   b. 77

   c. 82

   d. 88

10. Who set the Jets' record for receptions in a game by making 17 catches against San Francisco in 1980?

    a. Don Maynard

    b. Clark Gaines

    c. Bruce Harper

    d. Wesley Walker

11. Who is NOT one of the three receivers tied for the franchise record with 14 touchdown catches in a season?

    a. Brandon Marshall

    b. Art Powell

    c. Don Maynard

    d. Eric Decker

12. Who were the Jets playing when Wesley Walker set the franchise record with four touchdowns in a game?

    a. Buffalo Bills

    b. Miami Dolphins

    c. Pittsburgh Steelers

    d. New England Patriots

13. What is Mark Gastineau's single-season record for sacks?

    a. 22

    b. 21

    c. 19.5

    d. 18

14. The Jets' biggest victory in team history was a shutout of the Rams in 2008.

    a. True

    b. False

15. Who holds the record for most takeaways in his Jets career?

    a. James Hasty

    b. Darrelle Revis

    c. Larry Grantham

    d. Dainard Paulson

16. Who is the Jets' leader in career forced fumbles?

    a. John Abraham

    b. Larry Grantham

    c. Mo Lewis

    d. Calvin Pace

17. Pat Leahy, the Jets' all-time leading scorer, has twice as many points as anyone else in franchise history.

    a. True

    b. False

18. How many field goals did Jason Myers make against the Colts in 2018 to set the franchise record?

a. 5

b. 6

c. 7

d. 8

19. Who holds the Jets' record for most field goals made in a single season?

    a. Jim Turner

    b. Pat Leahy

    c. Nick Folk

    d. Mike Nugent

20. Who has the most punts in Jets history?

    a. Curley Johnson

    b. Lac Edwards

    c. Tom Tupa

    d. Chuck Ramsey

QUIZ ANSWERS

1. B – 496

2. D – Ken O'Brien

3. C – Ken O'Brien

4. C – 30

5. A – True

6. A – Emerson Boozer

7. C – 371

8. B – False

9. D – 88

10. B – Clark Gaines

11. D – Eric Decker

12. B – Miami Dolphins

13. A – 22

14. B – False

15. C – Larry Grantham

16. C – Mo Lewis

17. A – True

18. C – 7

19. A – Jim Turner

20. D – Chuck Ramsey

DID YOU KNOW?

1. All Jets quarterbacks are trying to replicate Joe Namath's success, but none of them has even thrown for 4,000 yards in a season since Namath did it in 1967. Ryan Fitzpatrick came the closest in 2015, falling just 95 yards short of the milestone, but it has been a challenge for the Jets to find a quarterback who can reach the 4,000-yard plateau. Only two quarterbacks since 1986 have even thrown for 3,500 yards—Fitzpatrick and Vinny Testaverde in 2000—and no one has even come within 40 yards of Namath's record for yards per game at 286.2 in that 1967 season.

2. Curtis Martin holds six of the top-10 single-season rushing marks in Jets history, including the three best seasons in franchise history. It will take a monstrous effort for someone to break Martin's franchise-record 1,697 yards from 2004, especially since Thomas Jones is the only other running back to rush for 1,400 yards in a season for the Jets. Martin's 2004 output broke his previous franchise record from 2001 when he became the first 1,500-yard running back in Jets history with 1,513 yards. That 2001 season topped the record he set in 1999 when he rushed for 1,464 yards, breaking Freeman McNeil's record by more than 100 yards.

3. Brandon Marshall's 2015 record-setting season was nothing more than him being a consistent receiver for the

Jets. Marshall had 10 games with at least 100 yards receiving, and he had at least three receptions in every game, yet he never had more than 131 yards in any single game that season. He caught a touchdown in 12 of 16 games that year to tie the team record with 14 touchdown catches. Marshall obliterated both the Jets' record for receptions with 109 (16 more than Al Toon in 1988) and receiving yards with 1,502 (68 more than Don Maynard in 1967).

4. Joe Namath had 15 fourth-quarter comebacks in his Jets career, which is the most in team history, but the legendary quarterback does not hold the record for most game-winning drives. That record belongs to Ken O'Brien, who had 16 game-winning drives in his Jets career. He had a league-best five game-winning drives in 1991 to lead the Jets to an 8-8 record, but only two of them required a fourth-quarter comeback. Namath had 15 game-winning drives in his career, including three in the 1968 Super Bowl season, but he had four fourth-quarter comebacks in 1966 for the Jets.

5. Larry Grantham might have been a linebacker, but he made a significant impact in the Jets' passing defense during his career. He leads all Jets linebackers with 24 career interceptions, tied for the fourth-most in team history. His 43 total takeaways is a team record, one more than James Hasty had during his career in New York.

6. Officially, Mark Gastineau holds the Jets' record with 74 sacks in his career but that total doesn't include the 33.5 he

had before sacks became an official statistic in 1982. Shaun Ellis is just 1.5 sacks behind Gastineau, though all of his sacks came when sacks were an official statistic. In two straight years, Gastineau led the league in sacks, with 19 in 1983 and then setting the franchise record with 22 the year after. He had 13.5 sacks in 1985 as he led the New York Sack Exchange in chasing down opposing quarterbacks.

7. Thomas Jones holds the non-kicker single-season scoring record in Jets history with 90 points in 2008 on 15 touchdowns (13 rushing and two receiving). Don Maynard's 88 receiving touchdowns and two 2-point conversions give him the career scoring record among non-kickers. Pat Leahy is the Jets' all-time scoring leader with 1,470 points, more than twice as many as Nick Folk, who is in second place with 729. However, no one has come close to topping Jim Turner's single-season scoring record from the Super Bowl season in 1968 when he averaged more than 10 points per game and finished with 145 points, 16 more than anyone else in Jets history.

8. Lachlan Edwards's booming leg and the poor Jets offense helped the punter record the top three punting averages in Jets history. In 2017, Edwards set the record with a 46.6 yards per punt average on 94 punts, the second-most in a single season behind Brian Hansen's 99 in 1995. In both 2018 and 2019, Edwards averaged 45.9 yards per punt, though his 2019 average was slightly higher than his 2018 average if you expand the decimal places. Both of those 45.9-yard averages are more than the 45.9 yards Ryan

Quigley averaged in 2014 to originally set the Jets' record for punting.

9. It wasn't that long ago that New York had its biggest win in franchise history, a 47-3 shellacking of the Rams in 2008. The Jets led that game 40-0 at halftime and had just 373 total yards from scrimmage in the game. Thomas Jones rushed for three touchdowns, Brett Favre threw two, Calvin Pace returned a fumble 50 yards for a score, and Jay Feely made four field goals to complete the scoring. The Jets have been on the wrong side of seven games that were decided by at least 41 points, none worse than the 56-3 beatdown the Patriots put on them in 1979. Pat Leahy's 30-yard field goal in the first quarter were the only points on the day for the Jets, who surrendered 597 yards of offense and allowed Steve Grogan to throw five touchdown passes in the win.

10. The Jets' biggest comeback came in 2000 when Miami held a 30-7 lead at the end of three quarters in the "Monday Night Miracle." Vinny Testaverde threw three touchdown passes, and John Hall kicked a field goal to tie the game with less than four minutes left. Yet the Dolphins had a long kickoff return and a long touchdown pass to reclaim the lead only for New York to charge down the field and score with less than a minute left. Hall then won the game with a 40-yard field goal on New York's first possession in overtime. The Jets have blown a 21-point lead four times in franchise history to set their own record for futility. The first one happened in 1983

when the Falcons stormed back from a 21-0 deficit in the middle of the third quarter to beat the Jets 27-21. Ten years later, the Jets raced out to an early 21-0 lead but ended up losing the game on a 94-yard interception return in the fourth quarter. The Colts overcame a 24-3 deficit in the third quarter to win in overtime in 1995, and the Patriots overcame an early 21-0 hole in 1996 to win 31-27.

CONCLUSION

Congratulations on reaching the end of this exciting journey through the history of the New York Jets. We hope you have reached this point filled with new facts about your favorite NFL team. Whether you learned more about the Jets or were able to expand your knowledge with behind-the-scenes information about your favorite players and moments, we hope you enjoyed this trip through the exciting history of the New York Jets.

Kermit the Frog was right, it isn't easy being green, but hopefully, the Jets' fortunes turn around in the near future. We tried to highlight the positives as much as we did the negatives in the Jets' football history. It is sometimes easy to forget just how many great players have played for the Jets and how many more great players the franchise might unearth in the near future. It hasn't all been doom and gloom for the Jets since Don Maynard and Joe Namath roamed the sidelines for Gang Green. There have been plenty of exciting moments around the frustrating feeling of being a Jets fan.

We designed this book for you, the fan, to be able to embrace your favorite team and feel closer to it. Maybe you weren't familiar with the history of the franchise and the process of how the Jets came to be. Perhaps you didn't realize how a few shrewd moves have made all the difference for the Jets in their history. Or maybe we just couldn't stump you at all and you're the ultimate New York Jets superfan. No matter how well you did on the quizzes, we hope we captured the spirit of the franchise and gave you even more pride for your team.

There are a lot of questions about the future of the Jets as they head into the 2021 offseason. Will New York be able to build around Sam Darnold to create a playoff-caliber team? Do the Jets need to hit the restart button with a new quarterback? How does a new leadership team deal with the consistent problems that have plagued the Jets since Rex Ryan left? There is no doubt that the Jets die-hards aren't going anywhere because New York sports fans are some of the most loyal in the world. The question is how quickly will the Jets be a team they can be proud to support again.

Made in the USA
Columbia, SC
09 December 2022

73219457R00076